Anxiety Disorders:
An Introduction

Caleb W. Lack

Anxiety Disorders: An Introduction
Copyright © 2013 Caleb W. Lack

Published by *Onus Books*

Printed by Lightning Source International

Cover design: Onus Books

Trade paperback ISBN: 978-0-9566948-7-4

OB 03/06

10 9 8 7 6 5 4 3 2 1

About the author:

Caleb W. Lack, Ph.D. is an Assistant Professor of Psychology and Counseling Practicum Coordinator in the Department of Psychology at the University of Central Oklahoma.

A clinical psychologist licensed to practice in both Oklahoma and Arkansas, Dr. Lack is the author of more than three dozen scientific publications relating to the assessment and treatment of psychological problems such as Obsessive-Compulsive Disorder, Tourette's Syndrome, pediatric mood disorders, and posttraumatic stress. In addition, Dr. Lack has presented nationwide and internationally at conferences on a variety of topics, including children's reactions to natural disasters, computer-based treatment of substance abuse, innovative teaching and training methods, and more. He is on the editorial board of several scientific journals and a reviewer for both journals and granting agencies.

Dr. Lack's clinical interest in evidence-based practice developed while in graduate school for Clinical Psychology at Oklahoma State University and during his predoctoral internship in Clinical Child/Pediatric Psychology at the University of Florida. He specializes in the treatment of children and adults with anxiety disorders (particularly obsessive-compulsive disorder), psychological assessment, and has extensive experience with persons with chronic tics and Tourette's Syndrome. He has consulted for and been interviewed by local, national, and international media outlets.

In addition to courses on his clinical and research specialties in the anxiety disorders and evidence-based psychological practice, Dr. Lack also teaches undergraduate and graduate courses on critical thinking, science, and pseudoscience. These recently culminated in the edited text *Science, Pseudoscience, & Critical Thinking* as well as a series of documentaries on pseudoscience and superstition in Oklahoma. He writes the "Great Plains Skeptic" column on the

Skeptic Ink Network (www.skepticink.com/gps), as well as presenting about skepticism and critical thinking frequently.

A native Oklahoman, Dr. Lack grew up in the rural community of Mountain View, where his parents still reside and farm and ranch on land that has been owned by the family for close to 100 years. He currently resides in Edmond, Oklahoma with his beautiful wife and brilliant son on a wonderful little property called Freethought Farm.

Learn more about Dr. Lack at www.caleblack.com

This book is dedicated to the hundreds of people I have seen over the past decade who qualified for one of the diagnoses in this book. It is my hope that this will allow others to better understand their struggles and how to assist them in improving their quality of life.

CONTENTS

What is a Mental Disorder?

The terms "mental disorder," "mental illness," and "psychopathology" are often used interchangeably by those in psychology and related fields; all refer to the study of unusual or abnormal behaviors that impair one's daily functioning. Unlike terms and concepts in many of the physical sciences, however, there is not a single, agreed-upon by all operational definition for these terms. The primary definitional conflict hinges on this question: Can mental disorders be defined as a scientific term, or are they instead socially constructed?

This lack of a single definition can lead to confusion and communication problems both when mental health professionals, such as psychologists, psychiatrists, counselors, or social workers, attempt to talk to each other and to the general public. As a result, mental disorders are used and defined in a variety of ways. Before beginning our examination of anxiety disorders, we must discuss these definitions and decide which one (or ones) will guide this book. Below are descriptions of the most common perspectives.

Mental Disorders as Statistical Deviance

The statistical deviance perspective has enormous common sense appeal, as it involves defining abnormal behavior by comparing an individual's behavior to the frequency of occurrence of the same behavior in the general population. A behavior is considered abnormal if it occurs rarely or infrequently in the general population. This definition lends itself very well to measurement, as researchers and clinicians can administer objective assessments to clients and get accurate measurements of just how far their depression, anxiety, hyperactivity, and so on are from the norm. As such, this definition is often seen as highly scientific.

Unfortunately, several problems are apparent when this model is examined closely. First, who determines how far from the norm is too far from the norm? It is not as if there is a stone tablet handed down from the psychopathology gods that has "Behaviors that are two or more standard deviations from the norm shall be considered abnormal" written on it. Instead, researchers and clinicians make that decision. Often, behaviors are considered "abnormal" if they occur in less than 5% of the population (1.645 standard deviations from the mean), but this is an entirely arbitrary cutoff. Another concern is that the tests that measure one's deviation are developed from within a particular cultural framework. In other words, there is not an objective, scientific definition of "obsessive-compulsive disorder," there is only the definition that the researchers developing the measure have (and someone else may not agree with it).

It is also worth noting that when viewing behavior, both sides of the normal curve would be considered "abnormal." So, according to this model, both someone with very high and very low general anxiety would be considered abnormal. In the real world, though, it is usually only one tail of the curve that is viewed as problematic or abnormal. For illustrative purposes, picture someone with an IQ of 70 and another person with an IQ of 130. On a scale where 100 is the average, with a standard deviation of 15, both are equally deviant from "normal" intelligence. Most people, however, would only consider the person with extremely low IQ to have a mental disorder, another problem with this conception.

Mental Disorders as Social Deviance

In the social deviance perspective, behavior is deemed abnormal if it deviates greatly from the accepted social standards, values, and norms of an individual's culture. This is different from the statistical perspective described above, as this method is uninterested in the *actual* norms of the population. This is because a population may have accepted standards that the majority of the culture do not actually meet. An example of this would be using alcohol and tobacco prior to the legal age of use, which would be considered unlawful and socially unacceptable, yet major surveys show that over 75% of high school seniors have consumed alcohol.

The problems with the social norms perspective are fairly obvious. First, there is little to no objective validity, due to individuals and groups even within the same culture having different ideas of what is socially acceptable. Second, what is acceptable at one point in time can become unacceptable with the passage of time, or vice versa. Until 1973, for example, homosexuality was classified as a diagnosable mental disorder by the American Psychiatric Association, rather than being recognized as a normal variation of sexual orientation. Finally, the different morals and standards of disparate cultural groups would mean that what was normal in one country or region would be considered abnormal in another.

Mental Disorders as Maladaptive Behavior

The maladaptive behavior perspective attempts to classify as mental disorders those behaviors that are dysfunctional. This refers to the effectiveness or ineffectiveness of a behavior in dealing with challenges or accomplishing goals. Typically discussed maladaptive behaviors include physically harmful behaviors, behaviors that prevent the person from taking care of themselves, those that prevent communication with others, and those that interfere with social bonding and relationships. As with our other perspectives, there are major concerns with this one.

First, how adaptive a behavior is hard to objectively quantify. This is due to the fact that the adaptive level of any particular behavior is based on both the situation and one's subjective judgment. If a person is engaging in coercive behaviors, stealing, and lying to others, most people would say those are maladaptive behaviors (and depending on his age, qualify you for a diagnosis of Conduct Disorder or Antisocial Personality Disorder). But what if you learn that he was doing this to obtain food or medicine for his family?

3

Would that still be maladaptive? One's culture also plays a large role in determining the adaptiveness of a behavior. For instance, in many Native American tribes, it is considered disrespectful to look an elder directly in the eye when talking to them. In other cultures, though, it would be considered disrespectful to *not* look them in the eye. Finally, this perspective clashes mightily with the statistical deviance perspective, in that statistically deviant behaviors (e.g., an IQ higher than 99% of the population) can be highly adaptive, and that numerous maladaptive behaviors (such as fear of public speaking) are quite common in the population as a whole.

Dimensional vs. Categorical Models of Mental Disorders

Another, different way to think about mental disorders is captured in the concept of categories versus dimensions. In a categorical model, psychopathology is dichotomous, either being present or not being present. In other words, you either have a mental disorder, or you don't, there is no in-between. Dimensional models, on the other hand, acknowledge the fact that the vast majority of human behavior exists on a continuum, rather than the polarized view of the categorical model. What tends to be labeled as abnormal and unusual are merely the far ends of this normal curve of behavior. In this model, then, mental disorders are just extreme variations of normal psychological phenomena or problems that many or most of us experience.

The dimensional model has a very large amount of scientific support, particularly in the area of personality disorders. Support has been found for dimensional models of many other disorders, though, including anxiety, depressive episodes, and even psychotic disorders. Unfortunately, however, the real-world often requires *caseness* or *non-caseness*. In many instances one must be diagnosed with a particular mental disorder to obtain certain things, such as insurance reimbursement, special services at school, or disability benefits. This, subsequently, creates a tension between the need for categories and the lack of scientific support for them.

DSM Definitions of Mental Disorder

The Diagnostic and Statistical Manual of Mental Disorders (DSM) is published by the American Psychiatric Association, and is the most widely used classification system of mental disorders in the United States (outside of the U.S., both the DSM and the International Classifications of Disease, or ICD, are used). It provides diagnostic criteria for almost 300 mental disorders. But how exactly does it define mental disorder? In the most recent edition, published in 1994, the following features are considered descriptive of a mental disorder:

a) A clinically significant behavioral or psychological syndrome or pattern that occurs in an individual

b) Is associated with present distress (e.g., a painful symptom) or disability (i.e., impairment in one or more important areas of functioning) or with a significantly increased risk of suffering death, pain, disability, or an important loss of freedom

c) Must not be merely an expectable and culturally sanctioned response to a particular event, for example, the death of a loved one

d) A manifestation of a behavioral, psychological, or biological dysfunction in the individual

e) Neither deviant behavior (e.g., political, religious, or sexual) nor conflicts that are primarily between the individual and society are mental disorders unless the deviance or conflict is a symptom of a dysfunction in the individual

The DSM-IV goes on to state, though, that "no definition adequately specifies precise boundaries for the concept of "mental disorder"" and that "the concept of mental disorder (like many other concepts in medicine and science) lacks a consistent operational definition that covers all situations." Even with those caveats, this definition has

5

considerable concerns: What exactly does "clinically significant" mean? How much distress is enough distress and who determines that? Who says what is or is not "culturally sanctioned"? And last, but perhaps most important, what defines a "behavioral or psychological syndrome or pattern"?

The categorical nature of the DSM-IV is also of concern, and the authors even state that they recognize the actual, dimensional nature of mental disorders, but due to the need for caseness (as described above) must operate in a categorical nature. This, in turn, contributes to the high amount of diagnostic overlap, or comorbidity, present in clinical populations. In one of the most well-conducted studies to examine this issue, Ronald Kessler and his research team (2005) found that 26.2% of Americans met criteria for a mental disorder; of these, 45% met criteria for two or more disorders.

These concerns and questions are certainly on the minds of many researchers and clinicians, and in fact a special group was assembled to rework the definition of a mental disorder for the upcoming revision of the DSM, the DSM-5, which is scheduled to be published in May 2013. The proposed revision, which was made available both online at DSM5.org and in an article by D.J. Stein and colleagues (2010), is as follows.

a) A behavioral or psychological syndrome or pattern that occurs in an individual
b) That reflects an underlying psychobiological dysfunction
c) The consequences of which are clinically significant distress (e.g., a painful symptom) or disability (i.e., impairment in one or more important areas of functioning)
d) Must not be merely an expectable response to common stressors and losses (for example, the loss of a loved one) or a culturally sanctioned response to a particular event (for example, trance states in religious rituals)

e) That is not primarily a result of social deviance or conflicts with society

As in the DSM-IV definition, there are other proposed caveats or considerations. A mental disorder should, by this definition, have diagnostic validity, clinical utility, and be differentiated from other, similar disorders. In addition, it is again acknowledged that there is no precise boundary between normality and mental disorders, and that the addition or deletion of a condition from the DSM should have substantial potential benefits which outweigh potential harms. While this proposed definition, and the revisions to many disorders that actually specify measures to determine severity and symptom level, are certainly an improvement over the DSM-IV (which was, in turn an improvement over earlier versions), there are still concerns over this definition. Specifically, will such severity indicators be used in real-world practice, and how will the introduction of such dimensionality impact treatment, reimbursement, and diagnostic practices? Will the improved diagnostic categories decrease the amount of overlap and comorbidity seen in mental health settings?

What to Do?

Given the problems with all of the preceding definitions of a mental disorder, one might begin to question the need for such a term or concept. After all, if it cannot be easily and accurately defined, what use is it? If the DSM categories are problematic, then why diagnose using them? The simple answer is "We use them because we need them."

Humans are natural categorizers, with a need to group and order things that we encounter. Our diagnostic typologies reflect this underlying need. It is much easier to understand and communicate to someone that a client is diagnosed with obsessive-compulsive disorder and generalized anxiety than to say something like "Their general anxiety level is at the 87th percentile, while they also have more obsessive, intrusive thoughts than 94% of the population and a subsequent rate of compulsive, anxiety reducing behaviors greater than all but 16% of their peers." In many cases, dimensional models of psychopathology, although perhaps more accurate, may simply be too confusing and/or complex to be useful in the real world.

Doing diagnostic work, and giving a patient a diagnosis based on presenting symptoms and lab findings, is an enormous part of all health professions. This is true even though dimensional models actually make more sense for almost all of what are called diseases (e.g., "Your blood pressure is higher than 95% of males your age, weight, and fitness level" rather than "You have high blood pressure.") Given clinical psychology's development and outgrowth from medicine, it makes sense that diagnosis would be part of our heritage. In many ways, it also establishes the credibility of psychiatry and clinical psychology by allowing these professions to stake out their "territory." Having something like the DSM essentially says "These problems and dysfunctions are the domain of psychiatry, so you other types of health providers back off." Losing diagnoses as part of the profession would mean that, in essence, we were losing our domain of health care. These reasons are, of course, in addition to the facts discussed previously about how real-life requires caseness or non-caseness in many occasions.

So, we as a profession and a society need definitions of mental disorders, and yet there does not appear to be a scientific consensus or definition on what a mental disorder actually is. So if there can be no truly scientific definition, what are we left with?

Mental Disorders as Social Constructions

Mental disorders, mental illness, and psychopathology are best understood as products of our history and culture, and should not try to be defined as some sort of universal, scientific construct. Mental disorders are, in a very real sense, invented. This does not, however, mean that they are not real. Instead, our conception of what is and is not normal behavior is influenced by everything from social and cultural forces, to politics and economics, to which professional groups have the most influence and clout at the time new definitions are being written. Mental disorders, then, are social constructs, a concept that is constructed by a particular group (in this case, the committee members of the DSM Work Groups, who are in turn influenced by researchers, clinicians, politicians, lay people, industry, religious beliefs, and more).

Accepting that mental disorders are a social construct, for some, implies that they are somehow fake or unimportant. Nothing, in fact, could be further from the truth. To put this in perspective, consider a number of other social constructs: love, beauty, race, poverty, wealth, physical disease. Each of those is constructed, and you will see different definitions of each when moving across time and between cultures. This does not rob any of them of their importance, or make any of them less real. The same is true of mental disorders.

As an example, consider a typical human and a virulent, invasive colony of *E. coli*: When certain strains are ingested by humans, and begin proliferating, it can cause an enormous amount of disruption to the host, so we (humans) label it as a bad bacterium. However, this organism is doing only what it has adapted to do, and is thus fulfilling the evolutionary directive to multiply and spread its genetic material. We have decided *as a society* that this species is bad, and our health is paramount over its health, and thus call it a disease and infection. This is social constructionism.

Conclusions

Mental disorders are hard to define, even by those who make it their life's work to study and treat them. Although there are certainly faults and flaws with the most widely used and social constructed definition, that of the DSM, the drawn boundary between normal and abnormal are essential to clinical psychology as a profession, persons with mental illness, and society as a whole.

Key References

American Psychiatric Association (2000). *Diagnostic and Statistical Manual of Mental Disorders, Fourth Edition, Text Revision.* Washington DC: Author.

American Psychiatric Association (2011). Definition of a mental disorder. Retrieved from http://www.dsm5.org/proposedrevision/Pages/proposedrevision.aspx?rid=465 on June 28, 2011.

Bergner, R. M. (1997). What is psychopathology? And so what? *Clinical Psychology: Science and Practice, 4*, 235-248.

Brown, P. (1995). Naming and framing: The social construction of diagnosis and illness. *Journal of Health and Social Behavior, 35* (Extra Issue), 34-52.

Eisenberg, L. (1988). The social construction of mental illness. *Psychological Medicine, 18*, 1-9.

Maddux, J.E., Gosselin, J.T., & Winstead, B.A. (2005). Conceptions of psychopathology: A social constructionist perspective. In J.E. Maddox & B.A. Winstead (Eds.), *Psychopathology: foundations for a contemporary understanding.* Mahwah, NJ: Lawrence Erlbaum Associates.

Stein, D.J., Phillips, K.A., Bolton, D., Fulford, K.W.M., Sadler, J.Z., & Kendler, K.S. (2010). What is a mental/psychiatric disorder? From DSM - IV to DSM - V. *Psychological Medicine, 40*, 1759 - 1765.
Widiger, T. A. (1997). The construct of mental disorder. *Clinical Psychology: Science and Practice, 4*, 262-266.

Introduction to the Anxiety Disorders

Anxiety is a common and essential process of daily life. It is highly important, evolutionary speaking, as people typically experience anxiety when faced with environmental threats such as encountering a lion (not so common a concern in modern society for most people), scarcity of food or other resources, or acceptance among one's peers and society at large. This anxiety orients the individual toward anticipating dangers, motivates the person to act in order to avoid events that might cause bodily harm or psychological distress, and prepares the body and mind for taking some sort of action. A complete lack of anxiety, in contrast, could cause someone to engage in potentially life-threatening and dangerous situations and not even be aware that they are dangerous.

When intense worry or fear begins to disrupt one's daily functioning, however, it can be detrimental to one's health. Anxiety disorders have the highest overall prevalence rate among psychiatric problems, with a 12-month rate of 18.1% and a lifetime rate of 28.8%. In any given year, over 40 million people in the U.S. are impacted by anxiety disorders, at a cost of over 46 billion dollars per year in increased medical expenses, lost productivity, and mental health expenditures. In fact, anxiety disorders alone account for over 31% of all mental health costs in the U.S. each year.

In addition to the monetary costs of the anxiety disorders, there are enormous impacts on quality of life (QoL) and functioning. For example, studies have shown higher incidence of divorce and martial strife, higher rates of financial problems and reliance on public assistance (e.g., disability, welfare), lowered educational achievement, and increased limitations in the types of jobs one is able to work. Meta-analyses have shown that the most damaging anxiety disorders to overall quality of life are social phobia and post-traumatic stress disorder (PTSD), but that all are associated with high rates of QoL and functional impairment, especially in the areas of mental health and social functioning.

Although highly related, fear and anxiety are different from each other in a number of ways. Fear is a response to a real danger and directed at a present threat, usually accompanied by escape behaviors, physiological arousal, and thoughts about the imminent threat. It also tends to be a highly biologically adaptive response, allowing one to avoid potential dangers and thus live to continue your genetic line. Anxiety, however, is usually more future-oriented and corresponds to a state of uncertainty or ambiguousness. It is often accompanied by avoidant behaviors, tension, and thoughts about a future threat. Commonalities of the two include the presence of cognitive appraisals of threat or danger and that they are (usually) adaptive to an organism. Also, anxiety often follows a fear reaction and conversely, repeated anxiety experiences can actually generate fear reactions. Many of the anxiety disorders fall onto one side or the other, although persons with social anxiety disorder seem to experience both in almost equal measure.

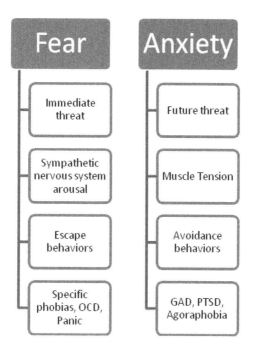

People who have been diagnosed with an anxiety disorder show a number of differences, both clinically and experimentally, from those without or with different mental disorders. For instance, elevated sensitivity to threats, preconscious attentional biases towards personally relevant threat stimuli, and biases to interpret ambiguous information in a threat-relevant manner are all highly present in this group. In addition, one can see elevated amygdala responses to specific and general threat cues in the highly anxious compared to control groups.

Culturally, anxiety disorders are seen around the world, although not always in the same way. For instance, rates of these disorders are generally similar in U.S. and European samples, but in comparison to non-European countries the U.S. shows higher 12-month prevalence rates of panic disorder, specific phobias, and social anxiety disorder. Interestingly, the lowest measured rates are found in East Asian and

African populations, both living in their native region and in the U.S. These differences may be due in part to cultural biases within the DSM criteria that place an emphasis on prototypical Western ways of experiencing anxiety. For example, there is a heavy emphasis placed on the psychological symptoms of worry in generalized anxiety disorder, while in many U.S. minority cultures the most commonly reported symptoms are more physiological. In DSM's social anxiety disorder, worries about offending others are very uncommon, and instead worries about embarrassing one's self are seen; this is prototypical of an individualistic, as opposed to collectivistic society. Finally, some research has shown that in cultures outside the U.S., people report panic attacks lasting much longer and being less unexpected than they are defined in the DSM.

As you read about the anxiety disorders, you will notice there are many similarities between them, particularly in terms of the likely causal factors and effective treatments. Generally speaking, there are two classes of efficacious treatments for the anxiety disorders: pharmacology and psychotherapy. Medications that inhibit serotonin reuptake are usually considered the "first line" drugs to prescribe, and are effective for many disorders. In terms of therapy, the research is clear that certain kinds of therapy, in particular the cognitive and behavioral therapies (CBT), are at least as equally effective as medication, and tend to have better long-term outcomes. The three primary CBT techniques are exposure with response prevention, cognitive restructuring, and relaxation training. Unfortunately, there is a large discrepancy between the effectiveness of treatments and the access to effective treatments, particularly CBT. More detail on treatment will be given with each discussed disorder.

The remainder of this section of the book will be devoted to specific anxiety disorders. For each disorder, the following information will be presented:

14

1. DSM-IV criteria (as reported in the DSM-IV-TR, published by the American Psychiatric Association in 2000)
2. Associated features (those things that are not part of the criteria, but are often seen in this population, commonly comorbid disorders, and impact of disorder on quality of life and functioning)
3. Child versus adult presentation (if and how the disorder presents different across the lifespan)
4. Gender and cultural differences (if and how the disorder varies between the sexes and around the world)
5. Epidemiology (the prevalence patterns of the disorder)
6. Etiology (what is known about the causes of the disorder)
7. Empirically supported treatments (those pharmacological and psychotherapeutic methods that have scientific evidence to back their use)
8. DSM-5 criteria revisions (when appropriate, there will be discussion of the reasons why the revisions are being proposed)

Key References

Baldwin, D.S., Anderson, I.M., Nutt, D.J., Bandelow, B., Bond, A. et al. (2005). Evidence-based guidelines for the pharmacological treatment of anxiety disorders: recommendations from the British Association for Psychopharmacology. *Journal of Psychopharmacology, 19*, 567–596.

Baloğlu, M. Abbasi, A., & Masten, W.G. (2007). A cross-cultural comparison of anxiety among college students. *College Student Journal, 41*, 977-984.

Craske, M.G., Rauch,M.D., Ursano, R., Prenoveau, J., Pine, D.S., & Zinbarg, R.E. (2009). What is an anxiety disorder? *Depression & Anxiety, 26*, 1066-1085.

Davis, T.E., May, A., & Whiting, S.E. (2011). Evidence-based treatment of anxiety and phobia in children and adolescents: Current status and effects on the emotional response. *Clinical Psychological Review, 31*, 592-602.

Gunter, R.W., & Whittal, M.W. (2010). Dissemination of cognitive-behavioral treatments for anxiety disorders: Overcoming barriers and improving patient access. *Clinical Psychological Review, 30*, 194-202.

Kessler, R.C., Demler, O., Walters, E.E. (2005). Prevalence, severity, and comorbidity of twelve-month DSM-IV disorders in the National Comorbidity Survey Replication (NCS-R). *Archives of General Psychiatry, 62*, 617-627.

Lewis-Fernandez, R., Hinton, D.E., Laria, A.J., Patterson, E.H., Hofmann, S.G. et al. (2010). Culture and anxiety disorders: Recommendations for the DSM-V. *Depression & Anxiety, 27*, 212-229.

Lowe, P.A. & Reynolds, C.R. (2005). Do relationships exist between age, gender, and education and self-reports of anxiety among older adults? *Individual Differences Research, 3* (4), 239-259.

Olatunji, B.O., Cisler, J.M., & Tolin, D.F. (2007). Quality of life in the anxiety disorders: A meta-analytic review. *Clinical Psychology Review, 27*, 572-581.

Stein, D.J., Phillips, K.A., Bolton, D., Fulford, K.W.M., Sadler, J.Z., & Kendler, K.S. (2010). What is a mental/psychiatric disorder? From DSM-IV to DSM-V. *Psychological Medicine, 40*, 1759-1765.

Generalized Anxiety Disorder (GAD)

DSM-IV-TR Criteria

A. Excessive anxiety and worry (apprehensive expectation), occurring more days for at least six months about a number of events or activities (such as work or school performance).
B. The person finds it difficult to control their worry.
C. An unrealistic fear or worry, especially in new or unfamiliar situations.
D. The anxiety and worry are associated with three or more of the following six symptoms (with at least some symptoms present for more days for at least the past six months). NOTE: Only one item is required in children:
   1. Restlessness or feeling keyed up or on edge
   2. Being easily fatigued
   3. Difficulty concentrating or mind going blank
   4. Irritability
   5. Muscle tension
   6. Sleep disturbance (difficulty falling or staying asleep, or restless unsatisfying sleep)
E. The focus of the anxiety and worry is not confined to features of an Axis I disorder, e.g., the anxiety or worry is not about having a panic attack (as in panic disorder), being embarrassed in public (as in social phobia), being contaminated (as in obsessive-compulsive disorder), being away from home or close relatives (as in separation anxiety disorder), gaining weight (as in anorexia nervosa), having multiple physical complaints (as in somatization disorder), or having a serious illness (as in hypochondriasis), and the anxiety and worry do not occur exclusively during post-traumatic stress disorder.
F. The anxiety, worry, and physical symptoms cause clinically significant distress or impairment in social, occupational, or other important areas of functioning.

G. The disturbance is not due to the direct psychological effects of a substance (e.g., a drug of abuse, a medication) or a general medical condition (e.g., hyperthyroidism) and does not occur exclusively during a mood disorder, a psychotic disorder, or a pervasive developmental disorder.

Associated Features

In addition to the diagnostic features above, people with GAD often report several other types of psychological and physiological symptoms. These can include trembling (particularly of the extremities), nervous twitching, feeling shaky, and muscle soreness (usually related to high levels of tension they are experiencing). They can also experience somatic symptoms such as sweating, hot flashes, nausea, diarrhea, or an exaggerated startle response. Symptoms of autonomic hyperarousal, like rapid heart rate, shortness of breath, and dizziness are not as common as in other anxiety disorders, such as panic disorder and post-traumatic stress disorder, but can be seen.

Comorbidity of other disorders and GAD is extraordinarily high, with epidemiological studies showing rates of 90% in the general population, and clinic studies showing rates between 45-98%. Major depressive disorder (MDD) is the single most common comorbid disorder, with some 60% of patients meeting diagnostic criteria for both. Other typical comorbids include the other anxiety disorders, sleep disorders, and chronic pain. These high rates of comorbidity have lead some to question if GAD should actually be classified as its own, separate disorder or if it is instead a prodrome (that is, a precursor to) or symptom of other disorders. It appears, based on current research, that it is properly classified as its own disorder for three primary reasons: it can be both reliably and validly diagnosed; non-comorbid GAD can be seen; and the high comorbidity rates may be an artifact of the DSM diagnostic criteria.

The impact of GAD on an individual can be devastating. Compared to the other anxiety disorders, individuals with GAD tend to show higher levels of social and occupational impairments. In terms of quality of life, GAD patients show decreases that are comparable to those with physical illness such as diabetes, hypertension, and congestive heart failure. Persons with GAD also tend to have much higher numbers of visits, and costs of visits, to physicians annually than do people without anxiety. In fact, over half of patients diagnosed with irritable bowel syndrome (IBS) have comorbid GAD diagnoses, and many of them are not aware of this.

Child vs. Adult Presentation
In children and adolescents, the anxieties and worries seen in GAD are often focused on their performance at school or in sporting events – situations when their performance is being evaluated or observed by others. There may also be a large concern about being punctual in social situations. Children with GAD may also show signs of being overly conforming, showing perfectionism, and being unsure of themselves. They may tend to redo tasks because they are dissatisfied with whatever they are trying to accomplish, which is generally an idea that realistically they cannot achieve, while constantly checking and changing things.

Retrospectively, many diagnosed with GAD as adults report having felt anxious all their lives, and over half of those who present for treatment report onset in childhood or adolescence. Onset after 20 years old is not uncommon, though. The course of GAD has traditionally been considered to be chronic, but recent research shows that under 80% of those with lifetime diagnosis do not have chronic, clinical levels of worry.

Gender and Cultural Differences in Presentation
The diagnosed prevalence rate of GAD in females is over double that of males. Lifetime prevalence ratios are 1 male to every 1.9 females, with 12-month ratios of 1:2.2. There are different patterns of comorbidity seen between genders as well, with higher rates of substance use disorders (particularly alcohol use) and antisocial

personality disorders seen in males. Females, in contrast, show higher numbers of comorbid anxiety and mood disorders. Interestingly, even when controlling for comorbid problems, females also show higher rates of disability than males. The group at highest risk for having GAD are females who are middle-aged, not married, and of low income.

Culturally, persons living in the U.S. who are of Asian, Hispanic, or African descent are at lower risk for having GAD than Caucasians. Some studies have shown that those of minority status in the U.S., as well as persons living in Eastern Asia, experience more of the somatic symptoms of GAD and report fewer psychological or worry symptoms. There is some research, however, that shows psychological symptoms are as present in Chinese and Vietnamese people, but that they must be specifically asked about, as these populations are more likely to concentrate on somatic complaints.

Epidemiology

GAD prevalence rates are quite high across a number of studies. The Epidemiological Catchment Area Study reported that the lifetime prevalence rates range from 4.1% to 6.6% for DSM-III criteria. The National Comorbidity Survey Replication, which examined DSM-IV criteria in the United States, reported a lifetime prevalence rate of 5.7%, with 12-month rates of 2.7%. Very similar rates are reported in European samples, with rates between 1.2-1.9% for current and 4.3-5.9% for lifetime prevalence.

Etiology

It is not entirely known what causes generalized anxiety disorder, but a number of factors likely contribute. Evolutionarily, anxiety is highly useful, as it prepares the body for "fight or flight" by activating the sympathetic nervous system. In GAD, like in other anxiety disorders, this activation appears to be in response to what *should* be non-anxiety provoking stimuli. In other words, people with GAD display a specific cognitive bias that causes them to attend heavily to potentially threatening stimuli, as well as interpret ambiguous stimuli as if it were threatening.

While GAD does not necessarily run in families, that does not mean there is not a role that genetics play in the disorder. Instead of a propensity toward GAD, children instead inherit a greater likelihood of expressing high levels of neuroticism and anxiety sensitivity. Indeed, genetic studies show that there is a high genetic overlap between GAD and major depression. The environment may be responsible for how this vulnerability is then expressed. Intriguingly, one environmental risk factor may be smoking cigarettes, as teenagers who smoke are 5-6 times as likely to develop GAD as non-smokers. Trauma and stressful events like abuse, death of a family member, divorce, or changing careers may also lead to development of GAD.

At the level of the brain, several neurotransmitters have been found to be linked to GAD (as well as a number of other disorders). Serotonin and norephinephrine have both been implicated, with the causal mechanism seeming to be a lack of receptor sensitivity to them. The amygdale is also disrupted in GAD, impacting the appropriate rely of sensory information to the rest of the brain. This may help to explain the threat-bias displayed by those with GAD.

Psychologically, the central and defining feature of GAD is worry (leading some to propose it actually be renamed "Generalized Worry Disorder). Where the typical, non-clinically anxious person spends approximately 15% of their day worrying, people with GAD may spend as much as 60% engaged in worry. For them, worry is an avoidant coping strategy which is maintained by two types of reinforcement. First, worry leads to decreased physiological and emotional reactivity in response to stressors, which means it is positively reinforcing. Second, it is also negatively reinforced, as the vast majority of worries and fears do not come true; people with GAD attribute these bad things as not happening *because* they worried about them. This not only maintains worry, but causes people to see it as a good, beneficial activity. Unfortunately, it also has negative consequences, particularly increasing the frequency of intrusive, anxiety-provoking mental imagery, which results in a sense of uncontrollability. This in turn makes the individual with GAD both more likely to worry and increasingly impaired by their worry. As for why people might worry more often in the first place, it appears to be due to a high degree of intolerance for uncertainty. Uncertain or ambiguous situations are often viewed as stressful and upsetting, unfair, negative, avoided at all costs, and interfering with one's ability to function. These negative association with uncertainty then cause people to begin worrying about encountering them in the future.

Empirically Supported Treatments

Treatment for GAD can be done both via psychotherapy and pharmacology. There are similar effect sizes seen for cognitive-behavioral therapies (0.7) and medications (0.6). Unfortunately, though, the majority of persons with GAD lack access to properly trained CBT clinicians, and other therapies (supportive, psychodynamic, humanistic) are just not effective. This leads to the majority of persons with GAD being treated with medication, which is actually less cost-effective and shows fewer long-term benefits than CBT.

In terms of medication, two primary classes of drugs are used: benzodiazepines (BZD) and antidepressants (AD). With BZD, such as alprazolam, bromazepam, lorazepam, and diazepam, are quite effective at relieving GAD in the short-term, but are discouraged for long-term use. This limitation is recommended due to potential for developing tolerance and subsequent abuse, as within 4-6 weeks of use they are generally no more effective than a placebo. The most common side effects of BZD are dizziness, drowsiness, decreased alertness, and poor concentration. The most commonly prescribed drugs for GAD are types of AD, such as fluoxetine, duloxetine, escitalopram, paroxetine, and sertraline. There is little evidence to suggest an enormous difference in efficacy between tricyclics (TCA), serotonin reuptake inhibitors (SRI), or combined serotonin-norepinephrine reuptake inhibitors (SNRI). While these take considerably longer to show a response, sometimes up to six weeks after beginning taking them for full effectiveness, they have little risk of addiction and can be discontinued relatively easily using a gradually stepped-down dosage. Side effects often seen vary depending on the specific drug, with TCA often having more severe profiles. Common TCA side effects include sedation, dry mouth, postural hypotension, while common SRI side effects are dizziness, nausea, disturbed appetite, and sexual dysfunction.

Psychotherapeutically, CBT vastly outperforms other therapeutic modalities, at both immediate post-treatment and long-term follow-up. There is a very low (under 10%) rate of dropouts in CBT. Interestingly, shorter dosages (8-10 sessions) have been shown to be equally effective as longer ones, with treatment gains seen up to two years after treatment has been discontinued. This makes CBT superior to medication in relapse prevention, as well as more cost effective. It is important to note, however, that although there are large effect sizes, especially compared to wait-list controls (1.09), that only about half of patients will have their worry drop to non-clinical levels. There are four traditional components to CBT for GAD: self-monitoring, applied relaxation training, cognitive therapy, and the rehearsal of relaxation and cognitive restructuring in the real world.

Self-monitoring teaches patients to objectively observe their anxious responses and note the triggers of worry. This is crucial because the earlier a patient can identify worry, the more effective the deployment of coping responses will be. In the relaxation training, patients are taught progressive muscle relaxation in session, then are required to practice it twice daily until they have mastered the ability to, on conscious demand, release muscle tension from their entire body. Once this mastery is obtained, they will then rehearse this skill in real-life situations. Cognitive therapy is used to help correct the negative, pervasive cognitive biases seen in GAD. This is done by 1) identifying how the patient is thinking and the beliefs about self, world, and future that underlie those thoughts, 2) evaluating the accuracy of those cognitions through examination of their logic, probability, and past evidence, 3) generating alternative, more accurate interpretations, predictions, and ways of believing, and 4) using these new perspectives whenever worry is detected and engaging in deliberate behavioral experiments to test if the worry is accurate or not. After relaxation and cognitive therapy are taught, the therapist will have the patient practice using these coping strategies in session by eliciting worry. In GAD, it is key to use intense imagery, not just verbal descriptions, to induce higher anxiety levels, as talking it out is analogous to worrying aloud, which suppresses the intensity of emotional reactivity.

Proposed DSM-5 Revisions

The proposed changes in GAD criteria for DSM-5 primarily reflect an increase and focus on worry as the defining factor of the disorder. By drawing more attention to this key aspect of GAD, and putting less emphasis on physiological symptoms, it is hoped that the diagnostic criteria will become more reliable and better able to differentiate from other anxiety disorders. Other major changes include the decrease of duration of worry from 6 to 3 months, and the number of symptoms aside from worry decreased from 3 to 1. While the duration decrease will likely increase the number of people who qualify for this diagnosis, the symptom drops have not been shown to do the same in research trials. Finally, adding an avoidance criteria to the diagnosis brings the criteria more in line with the other anxiety disorders and is supported by both research data and clinical opinion.

Key References

Andrews, G., Hobbs, M.J., Borkovec, T.D., Beesdo, K., Craske, M.G. et al. (2010). Generalized Worry Disorder: A review of DSM - IV Generalized Anxiety Disorder and options for DSM - V. *Depression and Anxiety, 27,* 134 - 147.

Baldwin, D., Woods, R., Lawson, R., & Taylor, D. (2011). Efficacy of drug treatments for generalised anxiety disorder: Systematic review and meta - analysis. *BMJ: British Medical Journal, 342.* Prepublication copy.

Newman, M. G., & Borkovec, T. D. (2002). Cognitive behavioral therapy for worry and generalized anxiety disorder. In G. Simos (Ed.), *Cognitive behaviour therapy: A guide for the practising clinician* (pp. 150–172). New York, NY: Taylor & Francis.

van der Heiden, C., Methorst, G., Muris, P. and van der Molen, H. T. (2011). Generalized anxiety disorder: clinical presentation, diagnostic features, and guidelines for clinical practice. *Journal of Clinical Psychology, 67,* 58–73.

Specific Phobia (SP)

DSM-IV-TR Criteria

A. Marked and persistent fear that is excessive or unreasonable, cued by the presence or anticipation of a specific object or situation (e.g., heights, blood, injections, animals). Specific anxiety and fear elicited by an object or situation and resulting in avoidance behaviors.
B. Exposure to the phobic stimulus almost invariably provokes an immediate anxiety response, which may take the form of a situationally bound or situationally predisposed panic attack. Children can show affects and characteristics when it comes to specific phobias. Children can show anxiety by crying, throwing tantrums, experiencing freezing or clinging to the parent that they have the most connection to.
C. The person recognizes that the fear is excessive or unreasonable. NOTE: In children, this feature may be absent.
D. The phobic situation(s) is(are) avoided, or else endured with intense anxiety or distress.
E. The avoidance, anxious anticipation, or distress in the feared situation(s) interferes significantly with the person's normal routine, occupational (or academic) functioning, social activities or relationships, or there is marked distress about having the phobia.
F. In individuals under age 18 years, the duration is at least 6 months.
G. The phobic avoidance associated with the specific object or situation are not better accounted for by another mental disorder, such as obsessive-compulsive disorder (e.g., fear of dirt on someone with an obsession about contamination), post-traumatic stress disorder (e.g., avoidance of stimuli associated with a severe stressor), separation anxiety disorder (e.g., avoidance of school), social phobia (e.g., avoidance of social

situations because of fear of embarrassment), panic disorder with agoraphobia, or panic disorder without agoraphobia.

The DSM-IV-TR categorizes five general types of SP:

1. Animal Type: These include fears of animals such as dogs, snakes, cats, bears, etc.
2. Natural Environment Type: These include fears of heights, storms, and being near a water source such as a river or lake.
3. Blood-Injection-Injury (B-I-I) Type: These include fears of seeing blood; receiving a blood test or injection; for the more serious types of this phobia, seeing an injection on television or talking about the act.
4. Situational Type: These include fears of situations such as driving, flying, elevators, and enclosed places.
5. Other Type: These include other specific fears, including fear of choking or vomiting after eating certain foods, fear of balloons breaking or guns going off, fear of clowns or midgets.

There is controversy over these divisions, however. Some research has shown that SP instead may be better divided into three primary clusters of animal, B-I-I, and a combined situational/natural environment type, while other analyses have found only two clusters: B-I-I and all others. Still other researchers contend that dividing the categories based on the type of emotion elicited by the phobic object, fear or disgust, is most accurate and clinically useful. Much more research is needed in this area to clarify this issue.

Associated Features

People with SP will often remember fearful experiences they encountered in a drastically exaggerated manner. For example, a person with a fear of dogs may remember a dog they once encountered as being larger and faster than it actually was, or baring its teeth viciously when it was only panting with an open mouth. They will often go to great lengths to avoid an encounter with the phobic object, affecting one's work, family, and social life. For instance, a job may require a person to fly for a business meeting, but a fear of flying could keep them from completing this job task and result in the loss of that job. Exposure to feared stimuli often causes significant physiological responses, such as dizziness, shortness of breath, increased heart rate, and even fainting.

Over 75% of individuals who are diagnosed with SP actually have multiple phobias, with over 50% reporting three or more. In animal and height phobias, there is a substantial comorbidity with major depressive disorder, but this relationship is not seen across the other types. Across all types, though, comorbid anxiety disorders are highly common, but not as high as in other types of anxiety disorders.

With the B-I-I type, a strong vasovagal fainting response is common, characterized by an acceleration of heart rate and elevation in blood pressure followed by rapid deceleration of heart rate and drop in blood pressure and not infrequent fainting. This is in direct contrast to the acceleration in heart rate and elevation in blood pressure seen in the other specific phobias. It has been hypothesized that these differences are a biological protection mechanism, as one would want the sympathetic nervous system to be highly activated for most phobic objects, in order to enable "fight or flight." In B-I-I, for instance if you were seriously injured and bleeding, sympathetic nervous system activation would cause the heart to beat furiously, pumping blood out of the wound and putting one at greater risk of death.

As illustrated in some of the examples above, SP can have quite a negative impact on a person's functioning. Both adults and youth with clinical-level phobias shower a lower overall quality of life (QoL) than those without SP. In adults, functional impairment in education and employment has been observed, as well as more work loss days and poorer physical and mental QoL.

Child vs. Adult Presentation

Children will often express anxiety associated with this phobias by freezing, crying, throwing tantrums, or by refusing to let go of a person they trust to protect them. Children seem to display a higher degree of response to perceived threats of their phobias than adults. However, the physical anticipatory response is higher in adults. Adults and teenagers are usually aware that their phobia is unreasonable, although younger children often will not be. Children with SP are more likely to show distorted thoughts and memories concerning past experiences with the feared stimuli than are adults, but whether this is a result of the fear or caused the fear in the first place is unknown.

Gender and Cultural Differences in Presentation

Females in general have about a 2:1 ratio to males for having SP, with between 21.2 - 26.5% of women and 10.9 - 12.4% of men meeting criteria. Animal, situational, and storm or water phobias are overwhelmingly female, while heights (60% female) and B - I - I (35 - 65% female) more evenly distributed. There appear to be few differences in type prevalence across SES, family structure, or age, though.

There is some research on cultural differences, but not much. For example, here in the U.S., African - Americans endorse SP at three times the Caucasian rate, as well as endorsing more animal phobias but fewer B - I - I phobias. Interestingly, persons of Asian and Hispanic heritage show lower rates than Caucasians. Around the world, the overall reported prevalence rates in Puerto Rico, Germany, Switzerland and New Zealand are extremely low. One thing to note is that a fear that is commonly present in a culture, such as a fear of magic or spirits, should not be considered a SP unless it is in excess for that particular culture.

Epidemiology

Rates of SP in the general population are very high, with a lifetime prevalence rate of 12.5% and 12-month rate of 9.1%. A natural decline in SP rates across the lifespan is seen, with rates in 18-29 year olds almost double that of persons over 60 (10.3% vs. 5.6% over a 12-month period). The rates for types of phobias vary dramatically, with natural environment the most occurring (8.9-11.6%), followed by situational (5.2 - 8.4%), animal (3.3 - 7%), and B - I - I (3 - 4.5%).

The onset age depends upon the type of phobia. Generally, animal (6.3 - 9.2 years), natural environment (6.5 - 13.6 years), and B-I-I (5.5 - 9.4 years) types develop in early childhood. Fear of heights and situational specific phobias (such as claustrophobia) typically develop during the late teenage years and early third decade of life (13.4 - 21.8 years).

Given these high rates, and the fact that treatment for SP works remarkably well (see below), it is surprising how few persons actually present to treatment for phobias. For example, in a college sample, 34% of students reported being "significantly" or "severely" afraid of spiders, but less than 1 in 5 of them was interested in seeking treatment. This is particularly sad given the average age of onset for most phobias is prior to adolescence, which means people are spending decades of their life being terrified by something that could be resolved in a short time.

Etiology

There are two possible frameworks to view the development of SP: associative and nonassociative. The associative model of SP developed from animal models of fear, with some of the earliest work being done by John B. Watson using only classical conditioning (the famous – or infamous – "Little Albert" studies). As knowledge about operant conditioning grew, however, Mowrer's two - factor theory of avoidance learning became highly influential. In this theory, fears develop initially via classical conditioning and are then maintained via the operant conditioning process of negative reinforcement. For example, a girl gets attacked by a dog, classically associating the dog with fear; she then goes out of her way to avoid dogs, such as crossing the street to avoid encounter one, not going into pet stores, or declining invitations to parties where the host has a dog, negatively reinforcing that avoidance. Vicarious conditioning can also play an important role in associative learning, via modeling (a child sees a parent display fear or disgust to stimuli, and then patterns his behavior after that), information transmission (hearing about how dangerous it is to fly due to terrorists), and visual observation of fear (watching someone else encounter a stimuli and display phobic reactions). The impact of these types of associative learning, however, appear to be strongly mediated by nonassociative factors, such as preparedness and innate fears.

Evolutionary preparedness is a nonassociative theory that we as a species may be genetically primed to fear certain stimuli, thanks to our evolutionary history. This would include commonly phobic objects such as snakes and reptiles, spiders, the dark, heights, and closed spaces. The theory is that, due to the inherent dangerousness of such things throughout the history of our species, those individuals with a natural tendency to avoid such things were more likely to survive and reproduce, passing on the genes related to such a behavioral expression. It would also help to explain why things that are actually more dangerous, such as guns and cars, but have been around a relatively short period of time are not seen in phobic individuals nearly as often. This is not to say, though, that people are born afraid of certain stimuli. Instead, we slowly acquire the competencies needed to deal with both fear predispositions and actual fears, with phobias being those predispositions or fears that are a) resistant to extinction or habituation and b) acquired through associative processes. As such, one's environment can work toward eliminating biologically relevant fears via the same processes that are at work in building them. As such, the reality seems to be that it is not whether a given fear is associative or nonassociative, but instead how much learning is needed to evoke that particular fear.

Empirically Supported Treatments

Unlike the other anxiety disorders, where there are both supported psychological and pharmacological therapies, the treatment of specific phobias is done only with psychotherapy. The gold - standard treatment for phobias is exposure with response prevention, specifically using Öst's "One Session Treatment" protocol. There are two phases in this therapy: assessment and treatment. First, the clinician conducts a diagnostic assessment using an evidence - based, multi - method and multi-informant approach. This would include a structured or semi-structured interview such as the Anxiety Disorder Interview Schedule (ADIS - IV), self - report, and behavioral avoidance tasks. Afterwards, a functional assessment follows to accomplish several goals. First, to determine any maintaining variables of the phobia that would impede treatment. Second, a fear hierarchy, which is a rank ordering of feared stimuli or situations from most to least fearful, is generated. Next, the hierarchy is used to catalog most severe and catastrophic cognitions associated with each stimuli or situation. The clinician also attempts, if possible, to determine the onset and course of the phobia. Finally, the assessment allows the clinician to build rapport and present the rationale for treatment.

During the treatment phase, the clinician primarily makes use of exposure with response prevention techniques, but also incorporates cognitive challenges, modeling, reinforcement, education, and skills training into therapy. Exposures are seen as a series of negotiated behavioral experiments based on the fear hierarchy constructed during the assessment phase. Starting near the bottom of the hierarchy, the patient gradually confronts more and more fear-provoking stimuli, guided by the therapist. Patients must show at least a 50% decrease in distress to each stimuli before moving on to the next one. Generally, the treatment phase will last around three hours, allowing for massed exposure to the fear stimuli. This is then followed by self- or parent-guided exposures for homework, which allows overlearning to occur and a complete extinction of the fear to happen. Success rates with this time of treatment are astounding, with effect sizes well over 1.0 and treatment gains maintained for years afterward.

Proposed DSM-5 Revisions

The proposed changes for SP are primarily wording changes, rather than substantive diagnostic changes. For example, the DSM-IV wording of "marked and persistent fear" is changed to "marked fear or anxiety."

Key References

Coelho, C., & Purkis, H. (2009). The origins of specific phobias: Influential theories and current perspectives. *Review of General Psychology, 13*(4), 335 - 348.

Davis, T., Ollendick, T. H., & Öst, L. (2009). Intensive treatment of specific phobias in children and adolescents. *Cognitive and Behavioral Practice, 16*(3), 294 - 303.

LeBeau, R.T., Glenn, D., Liao, B., Wittchen, H - U., Beesdo - Baum, K. et al. (2010). Specific Phobia: A review of DSM - IV Specific Phobia and preliminary recommendations for DSM - V. *Depression and Anxiety, 27,* 148 - 167.

Ollendick, T.H., Raishevich, N. Davis III, T.E., Sirbu, C. Ost, L - G. (2010). Specific Phobia in youth: Phenomenology and psychological characteristics. *Behavior Therapy, 41,* 133 - 141.

Seim, R. W., & Spates, C. (2010). The prevalence and comorbidity of specific phobias in college students and their interest in receiving treatment. *Journal of College Student Psychotherapy, 24*(1), 49 - 58.

Obsessive-Compulsive Disorder (OCD)

DSM-IV-TR Criteria

A. Either obsessions or compulsions:

Obsessions as defined by (1), (2), (3), and (4):

1. Recurrent and persistent thoughts, impulses, or images that are experienced, at some time during the disturbance, as intrusive and inappropriate and that cause marked anxiety or distress

2. The thoughts, impulses, or images are not simply excessive worries about real-life problems

3. The person attempts to ignore or suppress such thoughts, impulses, or images, or to neutralize them with some other thought or action

4. The person recognizes that the obsessional thoughts, impulses, or images are a product or his or her own mind (not imposed from without as in thought insertion).

Compulsions as defined by (1) and (2):

1. Repetitive behaviors (e.g., hand washing, ordering, checking) or mental acts (e.g., praying, counting, repeating words silently) that the person feels driven to perform in response to an obsession, or according to rules that must be applied rigidly

2. The behaviors or mental acts are aimed at preventing or reducing distress or preventing some dreaded event or situation; however, these behaviors or mental acts either are not connected in a realistic way with what they are designed to neutralize or prevent or are clearly excessive

B. At some point during the course of the disorder, the person has recognized that the obsessions or compulsions are excessive or unreasonable. NOTE: This does not apply to children.

C. The obsessions or compulsions cause marked distress, are time consuming (take more than 1 hour a day), or significantly interfere with the person's normal routine, occupational (or academic) functioning, or usual social activities or relationships.

D. If another Axis I disorder is present, the content of the obsessions or compulsions is not restricted to it (e.g., preoccupation with food in the presence of an eating disorder; hair pulling in the presence of trichotillomania; concern with appearance in the presence of body dysmorphic disorder; preoccupation with drugs in the presence of a substance use disorder; there is some presentation of a preoccupation with having a serious illness in the presence of hypochondriasis, or thinking that one is ill the majority of the time; preoccupation with sexual urges or fantasies in the presence of a paraphilia; or guilty ruminations in the presence of major depressive disorder).

E. The disturbance is not due to the direct physiological effects of a substance (e.g., a drug of abuse, a medication) or a general medical condition.

Specify if with poor insight (if, for most of the time during the current episode, the person does not recognize that the obsessions and compulsions are excessive or unreasonable).

Associated Features

Although a diagnosis of OCD requires only that a person either has obsessions *or* compulsions, not both, approximately 96% of persons experience both. For almost all people with OCD, being exposed to a certain stimuli (internal or external) will then trigger an upsetting or anxiety-causing obsession, which can only be relieved by doing a compulsion. For example, I touch a doorknob in a public building, which causes an obsessive thought that I will get sick from the germs, which can only be relieved by compulsively washing my hands to an excessive degree.Some of the most common obsessions include unwanted thoughts of harming loved ones, persistent doubts that one has not locked doors or switched off electrical appliances, intrusive thoughts of being contaminated, and morally or sexually repugnant thoughts. Commonly seen compulsions include hand washing, ordering or arranging objects, checking, praying, counting, and thinking good thoughts to undo bad ones.

Given that obsessions almost always trigger a compulsion, there are certain patterns of the two seen together. For example, contamination obsessions are almost always followed by some sort of compulsive cleansing, such as washing hands, taking a shower, or using hand sanitizer. There is some disagreement in the literature about just how many dimensions OCD symptoms fall into, with some finding four factors and others five based on different analytic techniques.

4-factor	5-factor
• Hoarding • Contamination/cleaning • Symmetry/ordering • Forbidden thoughts	• Hoarding • Contamination/ cleaning • Symmetry/ordering • Forbidden thoughts • Over-responsibility

Up to 75% of persons with OCD also present with comorbid disorders. The most common in pediatric cases are ADHD, disruptive behavior disorders, major depression, and other anxiety disorders. In adults, the most prevalent comorbids are social anxiety, major depression, and alcohol abuse. Interestingly, the presence of comorbid diagnoses predict quality of life (QoL) more so than OCD severity. Different primary O/C are also associated with certain patterns of comorbidity, in both adults and youth. Primary symmetry/ordering symptoms are often seen with comorbid tics, bipolar disorder, obsessive-compulsive personality disorder, panic disorder, and agoraphobia, while those with contamination/cleaning symptoms are more likely to be diagnosed with an eating disorder. Those with hoarding cluster symptoms, on the other hand are especially likely to be diagnosed with personality disorders, particularly Cluster C disorders.

Almost *all* adults and children with OCD report that their obsessions cause them significant distress and anxiety, as opposed to similar, intrusive thoughts in persons without OCD. In terms of QoL, persons with OCD report a pervasive decrease compared to controls. Youth show problematic peer relations, academic difficulties, and participate in fewer recreational activities than matched peers. Overall, there is a lower QoL in pediatric females than males, but in adults similar disruptions are reported. When compared to other anxiety disorders and unipolar mood disorders, a person with OCD is less likely to be married, more likely to be unemployed, and more likely to report impaired social and occupational functioning.

Daily, there are a number of problems that people with OCD face. One is the avoidance of situations in which the objects of the obsessions are present. For example, a person may avoid using public restrooms or shaking hands with people because doing so will trigger their contamination obsession, which will lead to them having to do a cleansing compulsion. Some people will not leave their homes because that is the only way to avoid objects and situations that will trigger their obsessions. Frequent doctor visits may also occur because they fear that something is wrong with them physically, just like a hypochondriac would feel. Feelings of guilt can also be present, along with disrupted sleep patterns and extreme feelings of responsibility. Self-medication may also be present in adults, with alcohol and sedatives the most often abused substances.

Child vs. Adult Presentation

Presentation of OCD symptoms is generally the same in children and adults. Unlike many adults, though, younger children will not be able to recognize that their obsessions and compulsions are both unnecessary (e.g., you don't really need to wash your hands) and extreme (e.g., washing hands for 15-20 seconds is fine, but 5 minutes in scalding water is too much) in nature. In young children, compulsions often occur without the patient being able to report their obsessions, while adolescents are often able to report multiple obsessions and compulsions. Children and adolescents are also more likely to include family members in their rituals and can be highly demanding of adherence to rituals and rules, leading to disruptive and oppositional behavior. As such, youth with OCD are generally more impaired than adults with the same type of symptoms.

Gender and Cultural Differences in Presentation

While OCD is equally present in males and females in adulthood (although some studies have found much higher rates in females), the disorder is heavily male in pediatric patients. There are some differences in comorbidity as well. Among men, hoarding symptoms are most often associated with GAD and tic disorders, but in women social anxiety, PTSD, body dysmorphic disorder, nail biting, and skin picking are more often observed.

There is strong evidence that cultural differences do not play a prominent role in presence of OCD, with research showing few epidemiological differences across different countries and even between European and Asian populations. Similar symptom categories are seen across cultures, but culture can impact the content of obsessions and compulsions. In Bali, for example, heavy emphasis on somatic symptoms and need to know about members of their social network is found. Perhaps the best example is in religious obsessions, which are very common. Type of religious upbringing has been related to different types of primary obsessions, such as emphasis on cleanliness and order in Judaism, religious obsessions in Muslim communities, aggressive aggressions in South American samples, and dirt and contamination worries in the United States. Worries about blasphemy and going to hell might be common in evangelical Christina societies, but would not be seen in a Buddhist background. It is also important to note that many cultures have rituals that are deep-rooted in their history and do not indicate OCD. It is only when these rituals exceed the cultural norms that OCD may be a concern.

Epidemiology

In the U.S., the lifetime prevalence rate of OCD is estimated at 2.3% in adults and around 1-2.3% in children and adolescents under 18. The 1-year prevalence of OCD in adults is 1.2% in adults and around 0.7% in children. There is a fairly substantial number of "sub-clinical" cases of OCD (around 5% of the population), where symptoms are either not disturbing or not disruptive enough to meet full criteria. As noted above, pediatric OCD is heavily male dominated, with some studies showing that there is an evening out within the genders by adulthood, and some showing that the numbers reverse and females become predominant.

Etiology

Family studies have indicated that OCD is modestly heritable for adult onset (27-47% of the variance in symptoms), but shows a much higher heritability for child onset (45-65%). These numbers, though, emphasize that environment is still a very important contributor to development of OCD. Biologically, dysfunctions of the neurotransmitters serotonin, glutamate, and dopamine are all implicated. Frontal cortico-striatal circuitry appears to mediated the presence of OCD, with over activity of the direct pathway from the ventromedial caudate to the globus pallidus and substantia nigra thought to be associated with OCD symptoms. This in turn disrupts functioning of the mediodorsal thalamus.

A recent field of inquiry has attempted to link sudden, pediatric onset of OCD to strep infections. Pediatric Autoimmune Neuropsychiatric Disorders Associated with Streptococcus (PANDAS) is a highly controversial area of research. Children with PANDAS are reported to develop obsessions, compulsions, and tics with no prodromal symptoms or indications during the course of a streptococcal infection, and these symptoms can be alleviated with treatment of the infection. As mentioned, this is a emerging and contentious idea, with many prominent researchers and clinicians not convinced by the evidence.

Psychologically, the most well-supported model for development of OCD is the cognitive-behavioral one. It proposes that obsessions and compulsions arise from dysfunctional beliefs that one holds; the greater the strength of the beliefs, the greater the chance that a person will develop OCD. One of the major research findings to support this idea is that unwanted cognitive intrusions are experienced by most people, with similar contents to clinical obsessions, but are not believed and as such cause little to no distress. Conversely, in people with OCD, these intrusive thoughts can become obsession if they are appraised as personally important, highly unacceptable or immoral, or posing a threat for which the individual is personally responsible. These types of appraisals will lead to high amounts of distress, which one then attempts to alleviate via compulsions. These compulsions result in anxiety reduction, but it is only temporary and actually reinforces the maladaptive beliefs that led to the negative appraisal in the first place, thus perpetuating the cycle of obsessions and compulsions. This model is the basis for CBT for OCD, which attempts to break this cycle of reinforcement and correct those negative appraisals and maladaptive beliefs.

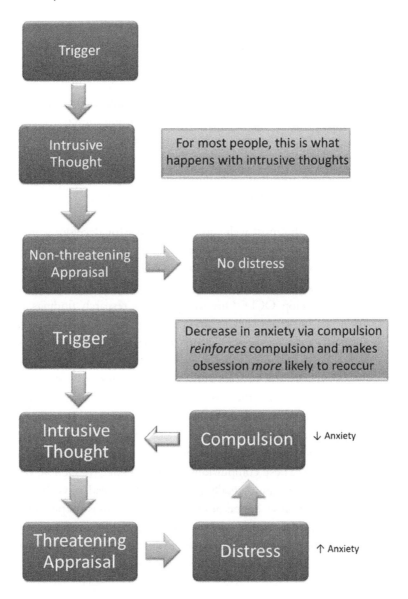

Empirically Supported Treatments

There are both pharmacological and psychological treatments for OCD that are supported by research evidence. Overall, pharmacology with serotonin reuptake inhibitors (SRIs) shows large effect sizes in adults (0.91), but only moderate effect sizes in youth (0.46). Even with effective medication, most treatment responders show residual symptoms and impairments. There is also a very high relapse rate seen across numerous studies (between 24-89%). SRIs can be supplemented with adjunctive antipsychotics, but only a third of patients will show improvements. Across subtypes of OCD, there are medication differences seen. For example, the presence of tics appears to decrease selective SRI effects in children, but it is unclear if it has the same effect in adults. Another known difference is that OCD with comorbid tics responds better to neuroleptics than OCD without tics does.

The treatment of choice for OCD, in both adults and children and backed by numerous clinical trials, is cognitive-behavioral therapy, particularly the exposure with response prevention aspect of it (EX/RP). It is superior to medications alone, with effect sizes ranging from 1.16-1.72. There is a low (12%) relapse rate, but it is important to note that up to 25% of patients will drop out prior to completion of treatment due to the nature of treatment. The structure of treatment is very similar to what is used to treat phobias, but the course of therapy generally lasts between 12-16 sessions due to the larger number of anxiety/obsession triggering stimuli. It has been found that those with hoarding cluster symptoms respond less well to CBT, in part due to reluctance to engage in exposures. For them and others who are not engaging in exposures as needed, a treatment module focusing on motivational enhancement may be required. Research has also shown that individuals with comorbidity respond equally well to treatment, and that treatment of OCD often results in decreases of other anxious and depressive symptoms. Intriguingly, group therapy that uses CBT and EX/RP has been shown to be equally as effective as individual therapy and, for persons with mild OCD, computer-assisted self-treatment has been shown to be very effective (e.g., BT-STEPS).

As with OST for phobias, the first step is an assessment to determine maintaining factors (such as family accommodation) and comorbid problems. Next, education about the causes (biological and psychological) of OCD is presented, and misattributions about causes are corrected, and patients are asked to keep track of all possible O/C symptoms over the course of a week, as this allows for construction of a fear hierarchy to begin. Different O/C symptoms are often interwoven in hierarchy, as most people will present with two or more symptom clusters (e.g., symmetry and contamination, or hoarding and forbidden thoughts). The therapist and patient work on hierarchy construction together, based on self-report, other-report (e.g. parents), and behavioral observations. Once the hierarchy is constructed, items on it begin to be addressed in therapy, starting with moderately difficult situations, as ones below will show decreases naturally with treatment of higher problems. During the treatment phase, the clinician makes use of EX/RP techniques, including both imaginal and *in vivo* exposures. Imaginal exposures are often used in the beginning to demonstrate that anxiety *will* decrease across time, or when the person has abstract worries and fears that are difficult to perform real-life exposures for. This also allows for practicing coping skills (e.g., cognitive restructuring and thought challenging) before confronting the real situation or stimuli. *In vivo* exposures follow and are similar to those conducted for persons with phobias, with the incorporation of cognitive challenges, modeling, reinforcement, and education into each exposure. Between sessions, homework is critical to the success of CBT for OCD, with the therapist helping the client to plan exposures to perform throughout the week, usually variations on what was accomplished during therapy. Ideal exposures are prolonged, repeated, prevent the use of distraction behaviors and show a SUDs decrease of at least 50% (with more being better). There may need to be shaping up to the more difficult situations, in terms of both time and use of distracters.

For example, a person may need to move from just standing in a public restroom, to touching the door, then the door handle, then the floor, then the top of the toilet, to the toilet handle, the toilet seat, and finally into the bowl.

Proposed DSM-5 Revisions

Several changes have been proposed to the diagnosis of OCD, primarily just wording changes such as clarifying that the O/C are time consuming and impairing. The largest change is in the specifiers, which will move from the dichotomous "with poor insight" to a more continuum-based assessment rated from "good or fair" to "poor" to "absent" insight. In addition, the specifer of "tic-related OCD"will be used if the patient has a lifetime history of a chronic tic disorder or Tourette's Syndrome. This has been proposed because this appears to be a distinct subtype of OCD and may account for up to 40% of pediatric cases. This category is often male-dominated, with a high incidence of symmetry/exactness/ordering and lower cleaning/contamination symptoms than seen in the general OCD population. In terms of comorbidity, there are very high rates of trichotillomania and disruptive behavior disorders seen in this subtype.

Key References

Abramowitz, J.S., Taylor, S., & McKay, D. (2009). Obsessive-compulsive disorder. *Lancet, 374,* 491-499.

Abramowitz, J.S., Whiteside, S.P., & Deacon, B.J. (2005). The effectiveness of treatment for pediatric obsessive-compulsive disorder: A meta-analysis. *Behavior Therapy, 36,* 55-63.

Lack, C.W., Storch, E.A., Keely, M., Geffken, G.R., Ricketts, E., et al. (2009). Quality of life in children and adolescents with Obsessive-Compulsive Disorder. *Social Psychiatry and Psychiatric Epidemiology, 44,* 935-942.

Leckman, J.F., Denys, D., Simpson, H.B., Mataix-Cols, D., Hollander, E. et al. (2010). Obsessive-compulsive disorder: A review of the diagnostic criteria and possible subtypes and dimensional specifiers for DSM-V. *Depression and Anxiety, 27,* 507-527.

Storch, E.A., Lewin, A.B., Farrell, L., Aldea, M.A., Reid, J.A. et al. (2010). Does cognitive-behavioral therapy response among adults with obsessive–compulsive disorder differ as a function of certain comorbidities? *Journal of Anxiety Disorders, 24,* 547-554.

Post-Traumatic Stress Disorder (PTSD)

DSM-IV-TR Criteria

A. The person has been exposed to a traumatic event in which both of the following have been present:

1. The person experienced, witnessed, or was confronted with an event or events that involved actual or threatened death or serious injury, or a threat to the physical integrity of self or others

2. The person's response involved intense fear, helplessness, or horror. NOTE: In children, this may be expressed instead by disorganized or agitated behavior.

B. The traumatic event is persistently reexperienced in one (or more) of the following ways:

1. Recurrent and intrusive distressing recollections of the event, including images, thoughts, or perceptions. NOTE: In young children, repetitive play may occur in which themes or aspects of the trauma are expressed.

2. Recurrent distressing dreams of the event. NOTE: In children, there may be frightening dreams without recognizable content.

3. Acting or feeling as if the traumatic event were recurring (includes a sense of reliving the experience, illusions, hallucinations, and dissociative flashback episodes, including those that occur upon awakening or when intoxicated). NOTE: In young children, trauma-specific reenactment may occur.

4. Intense psychological distress at exposure to internal or external cues that symbolize or resemble an aspect of the traumatic event.

5. Physiological reactivity on exposure to internal or external cues that symbolize or resemble an aspect of the traumatic event.

C. Persistent avoidance of stimuli associated with the trauma and numbing of general responsiveness (not present before the trauma), as indicated by three (or more) of the following:
1. Efforts to avoid thoughts, feelings, or conversations associated with the trauma
2. Efforts to avoid activities, places, or people that arouse recollections of the trauma
3. Inability to recall an important aspect of the trauma
4. Markedly diminished interest or participation in significant activities
5. Feeling of detachment or estrangement from others
6. Restricted range of affect (e.g., unable to have loving feelings)
7. Sense of a foreshortened future (e.g., does not expect to have a career, marriage, children, or a normal life span)

D. Persistent symptoms of increased arousal (not present before the trauma), as indicated by two (or more) of the following:
1. Difficulty falling or staying asleep
2. Irritability or outbursts of anger
3. Difficulty concentrating
4. Hypervigilance
5. Exaggerated startle response

E. Duration of the disturbance (symptoms in Criteria B, C, and D) is more than one month.

F. The disturbance causes clinically significant distress or impairment in social, occupational, or other important areas of functioning.

In addition, clinicians specify if the PTSD is acute (duration of symptoms is less than 3 months) or chronic (duration of symptoms is 3 months or more) and if it was a delayed onset (if onset of symptoms is at least 6 months after the stressor).

Associated Features

In addition to the diagnostic criteria, individuals with PTSD often describe feelings of guilt about surviving when others did not survive or about the things they had to do to survive a trauma. A number of other symptoms can occur, such as feelings of shame, despair, or hopelessness; feeling permanently damaged; a loss of previously sustained beliefs, social withdrawal; impaired relationships with others; or a marked shift from the individual's previous personality. Especially problematic are the self-destructive behaviors that can develop with PTSD, such as alcohol and drug abuse, suicidal behaviors, and risky sexual behavior.

Avoidance of situations or activities that remind a person of the trauma can cause functional impairment, problems with interpersonal relationships, and lead to marital conflict, divorce, or loss of job. Some individuals become greatly limited in the places and activities that they are able to engage in due to avoidance. Compared to healthy controls, people with PTSD report having a greatly reduced quality of life, and are at an elevated risk of poor physical health.

Having PTSD also puts one at a greatly elevated risk of developing comorbid disorders, even when compared to people with other anxiety disorders. Data indicate that over 80% of people with PTSD meet criteria for at least one other diagnosis, with over 50% having two or more comorbids. In persons with PTSD, high rates of simple (31%) and social phobias (27%) are seen, but the most commonly co-occurring disorders are non-anxiety ones, particularly major depression (48%) and substance abuse. Over 50% of males and almost 30% of females meet criteria for alcohol abuse or dependence, while other drug abuse is present in over 34% of males and 27% of females. In studies examining males veterans, even higher comorbidity rates are found for major depression, with 86% meeting criteria, but similar rates of anxiety and substance abuse problems were found.

Child vs. Adult Presentation

Exposure to traumatic events can have major developmental influences on children. While the majority of children will not develop PTSD after a trauma, best estimates from the literature are that around a third of them will, higher than adult estimates. Some reasons for this could include more limited knowledge about the world, differential coping mechanisms employed, and the fact that children's reactions to trauma are often highly influenced by how their parents and caregivers react. These impact the development and presentation of PTSD, leading to differences not only from adults, but within different age groups of children. In the weeks after a trauma, up to 90% of children may experience heightened physiological arousal, diffuse anxiety, survivor guilt, and emotional lability. These are all normal reactions and should be understood as such (similar things are seen in adults. Those children still having these symptoms three or four months after a disaster, however, may be in need of further assessment, particularly if they show the following symptoms as well. In children under the age of six, these may indicate problematic adjustment to the disaster: generalized anxiety about separation, strangers, or sleep problems; avoidance of certain situations; preoccupation with certain symbols / words; limited emotional expression or play activities; and loss of previously acquired skills. For older children, warning signs of problematic adjustment include: repetitious play reenacting a part of the disaster; preoccupation with danger or expressed concerns about safety; sleep disturbances and irritability; anger outbursts or aggressiveness; excessive worry about family or friends; school avoidance, particularly involving somatic complaints; behaviors characteristic of younger children; and changes in personality, withdrawal, and loss of interest in activities.

Gender and Cultural Differences in Presentation

Women are significantly more likely to develop PTSD after a traumatic experience than men, even when predominantly female victim traumas, such as sexual crimes, are taken into account, with lifetime prevalence rates well over double that for men (9.6% vs. 3.6%). The genders also show differential patterns of response to traumas. For example, only 1% of males threatened with a weapon will develop PTSD, but over 30% of females in similar situations will. Females also show higher rates after physical and sexual assaults.

The majority of studies have been done by Western researchers using Western populations. As such, we have only a small body of literature to draw cross-cultural comparisons. There has been some research showing that African Americans returning from the Vietnam War more at risk of developing PTSD than Caucasians or other minorities. Subsequent findings found that, for the overall population, African Americans and Native Americans are at a higher risk than other minorities for developing PTSD. Much of the cross-cultural research around the globe has focused on differential rates of PTSD, with major findings indicating that (as in the U.S.) the more traumas one is exposed to, the greater likelihood of developing PTSD.

There have also been considerable critiques of the application of PTSD, with its inherent Western biases, to non-Western cultures. Twelve-month prevalence rates vary greatly between the U.S. (3.6%) and most other countries, such as urban China (0.2%), Japan (0.4%), Mexico (0.6%), and even Europe (0.9%) and Australia (1.3%). These large differences have led many to advocate for the use of more localized, culture-specific stress reactions (such as *ataque de nervios* in certain Latin and Hispanic cultures). Using biomarkers (such as exaggeration of startle response or physiological reactivity) has also been proposed, but there is only preliminary data so support their use at this time.

Epidemiology

The majority of people experience some sort of traumatic event at least once during their lifetime, with 25% of people experiencing multiple traumas. Rates are slightly higher for men (61%) than for women (51%), although types of trauma vary dramatically between genders. Women, for example, are much more likely to experience sexual assault or rape (9%) than males (1%), but men are much more likely to be involved in a serious accident (25% vs. 14%). Thankfully, though, the prevalence rate for PTSD is much lower than these numbers, as the vast majority of those involved in traumatic experiences do not develop it. Lifetime prevalence rate for the general U.S. population is 6.8%, with 12-month rates of only 3.6%.

Not all groups are equally at risk of developing PTSD, however. In high- or at-risk individuals (e.g., combat veterans, disaster victims, or criminal violence), prevalence rates ranging from 3% to 58% have been found. In countries with high rates of civil war and internal strife, shockingly high rates of PTSD have been found. In one study, over 37% of Algerians in the late 1990s met criteria for a PTSD diagnosis, compared to 6.8% of Americans. Interestingly, the type of disaster a person experiences greatly impacts the chance of developing PTSD. For example, while only 4-5% of those who live through a natural disaster develop PTSD, studies have found that 30% or more of people involved in man-made disasters (shootings, bombings, and so on) develop PTSD.

In recent U.S. combat veterans, studies have found that lifetime prevalence is about 39% in males, above the rate of 30% seen in veterans of the Vietnam War. When compared to other types of traumas that males experience, being in combat results in higher lifetime PTSD prevalence, a greater likelihood of delayed onset, and a greater likelihood of unresolved symptoms. Several studies examining PTSD in military females have found similar rates, even without the front-line combat experience. These studies have been criticized, though, due to some methodological difficulties.

Etiology

Alone among all the disorders listed in the DSM, PTSD has a specific etiological event – experiencing a trauma. While it is highly adaptive to have a strong fight-or-flight response during a trauma and when your life is threatened, these reactions should decrease once the trauma has passed. In persons with PTSD, however, they do not. As such, PTSD can be seen essentially as a failure to adapt to differing situations. Why people's reactions fail to return back to normal after can be influenced by a number of factors. Prior to the event, a number of factors will greatly increase risk. These include being female, of a minority race, having a lower level of education, and having a lower income level. Also, a history of previous psychiatric problems and childhood trauma make it more likely that one will develop problematic symptoms. In addition to the type of trauma experienced, certain factors about the trauma can increase risk, such as greater perceived threat or danger and helplessness, as well as the unpredictability and uncontrollability of traumatic event. Post-trauma, lack of social support, overall amount of life stress, coping mechanisms used, and type of attributions made for the disaster can all increase risk.

Empirically Supported Treatment

As with most anxiety disorders, both medications and therapy can be effective in treating PTSD, although certain psychotherapies are much more effective. Meta-analyses show that CBT, particularly Prolonged Exposure (PE) and Cognitive Processing Therapy (CPT), have much greater overall effect sizes than medications for both self-reported symptoms (1.2 vs. 0.65) and clinician ratings (1.5 vs. 1.05). Nonetheless, medication can certainly be a very useful adjunctive treatment, especially to assist in controlling comorbid problems such as depression, and is more widely available than therapists trained in PE or CPT. The SSRIs (such as citalopram, fluoxetine, paroxetine, and sertraline) are the most well-studied group of agents, and have been shown to significantly outperform placebos in both civilian and military populations. The drug with the highest effect sizes, though, is venlafaxine, a SNRI. It slightly outperforms the SSRIs in both populations.

The two most well-supported psychotherapies are both types of CBT: prolonged exposure and cognitive processing therapy. They both share general components of psycho-education, anxiety management, exposure with response prevention, and cognitive restructuring. Little is known about their relative efficacy, but there is some research showing that clients with strong guilt about the trauma may fare better in CPT. Dropout rates are similar and relatively low across treatments.

The first part of PE is psycho-educational and allows the client to learn about trauma and its effects on individuals, as well as understand the symptoms of PTSD. This also lays out the groundwork and rationale behind why exposing oneself to the memories and to particular stimuli (both of which they are actively avoiding) is going to eventually lead to symptom reduction. Next, the client learns breathing skills to help control their anxiety and distress they will experience during the exposures. The third component is *in vivo* EX/RP, where a hierarchy of feared and avoided stimuli that are actually safe is developed, then increasingly anxiety-provoking stimuli are encountered and endured until they do not trigger anxiety in the individual. Finally, the fourth component of PE is mental exposure to trauma. This is accomplished by repeatedly having the person imagine the event as it occurred and experience all of the sights, the sounds, the smells, and perceptions of that event. This is often accomplished by writing trauma narratives, detailed descriptions of the trauma that would be read aloud repeatedly.

There are significant overlaps between PE and CPT, but also differences. The first CPT phase provides education about PTSD, but with an emphasis on the role of thoughts and how one's perceptions or beliefs influence the way that they feel. The second phase focuses on processing the trauma and can be done with or without a trauma account. There is a more historical focus in CPT, where the client is focusing on reflections of how they made sense of what happened to them and then being led to a different and more adaptive interpretation of the trauma. In the third component, cognitive restructuring is taught, allowing the client is to challenge their own negative and maladaptive thoughts and interpretations. The fourth and final component is focused on employing cognitive restructuring for both historical and current interpretations.

Proposed DSM-5 Revisions

In the DSM-5, it has been proposed that, given the differential presentation of PTSD across the lifespan, completely separate criteria be adopted for different age groups. In particular, distinctions between the presentation of PTSD in adults, adolescents, school-age, and preschool children have been discussed. This is primarily driven by the fact that the DSM-IV criteria were developed for and tested on older adolescents and adults. As such, the proposed criteria include large numbers of notes that describe developmentally appropriate symptoms (such as repetitive play reflecting the trauma or frightening dreams with no specific content), as well as lower number of symptoms required to meet diagnosis. The other major change proposed is the removal of DSM-IV Criterion A2 ("The person's response involved intense fear, helplessness, or horror.") as it has not been found to have either clinical or research utility.

Key References

Hembree, E.A., Rauch, S., & Foa, E.B. (2003). Beyond the manual: The insider's guide to prolonged exposure therapy for PTSD. *Cognitive and Behavioral Practice, 10*, 22-30.

Friedman, M. J., Resick, P. A., Bryant, R. A. and Brewin, C. R. (2011), Considering PTSD for DSM-5. Depression and Anxiety. doi: 10.1002/da.20767

Hinton, D.E., & Lewis-Fernandez, R. (2010). The cross-cultural validity of posttraumatic stress disorder: Implications for DSM-V. *Depression and Anxiety, 27*, 1-19.

Lack, C.W., Doan, R., & Young, P. (2010). Working with children in schools after traumatic events. In J.E. Warnick, K. Warnick, & A. Laffoon, (Eds.). *Educational policy and practice: The good, the bad and the pseudoscience. Volume II: Applied practices.* Hauppauge, NY: Nova Science Publishers.

Powers, M. B., Halpern, J. M., Ferenschak, M. P., Gillihan, S. J., & Foa, E. B. (2010). A meta-analytic review of prolonged exposure for posttraumatic stress disorder. *Clinical Psychology Review, 30*, 635-641.

Scheeringa, M. S., Zeanah, C. H. and Cohen, J. A. (2011), PTSD in children and adolescents: toward an empirically based algorithm. Depression and Anxiety. doi: 10.1002/da.20736

Social Phobia (SP)

DSM-IV-TR criteria

A. A marked and persistent fear of one or more social or performance situations in which the person is exposed to unfamiliar people or to possible scrutiny by others. The individual fears that he or she will act in a way (or show anxiety symptoms) that will be humiliating or embarrassing. NOTE: In children, there must be evidence of the capacity for age-appropriate social relationships with familiar people and the anxiety must occur in peer settings, not just in interactions with adults.

B. Exposure to the feared social situation almost invariably provokes anxiety, which may take the form of a situationally bound or situationally predisposed panic attack. NOTE: In children, the anxiety may be expressed by crying, tantrums, freezing, or shrinking from social situations with unfamiliar people.

C. The person recognizes that the fear is excessive or unreasonable. NOTE: In children, this feature may be absent.

D. The feared social or performance situations are avoided or else endured with intense anxiety or distress.

E. The avoidance, anxious anticipation, or distress in the feared social or performance situation(s) interferes significantly with the person's normal routine, occupational (academic) functioning, or social activities or relationships, or there is marked distress about having the phobia.

F. In individuals under age 18 years, the duration is at least 6 months.

G. The fear or avoidance is not due to the direct psychological effects of a substance (e.g., a drug of abuse, a medication) or a general medical condition and is not better accounted for by another mental disorder (e.g., panic disorder with or without agoraphobia, separation anxiety disorder, body dysmorphic disorder, a pervasive developmental disorder, or schizoid personality disorder).

H. If a general medical condition or another mental disorder is present, the fear in Criterion A is unrelated to it, e.g., the fear is not of stuttering, trembling in Parkinson's disease, or exhibiting abnormal eating behavior in anorexia nervosa or bulimia nervosa.

In addition, the DSM-IV has the "Generalized" specifier, where the person's fear includes almost all social situations.

Associated Features
Also known as Social Anxiety Disorder, persons with SP are often hypersensitive to criticism, greatly fear negative evaluation, have increased perceptions of rejection, difficulty being assertive, and low self-esteem or feelings of inferiority. Test taking can be difficult for individuals with social phobia due to their fear of indirect evaluation by others. Observable signs of anxiety (poor eye contact, making sounds like "uh" and "um" during speech) are often present in individuals with this disorder. Attending school or work may also be difficult for people with social phobia and they tend to underachieve in these areas.

Comorbidity within persons diagnosed with SP is very high, over 80% in clinical settings. In adults, the most commonly diagnosed comorbids are major depression, dysthymia, panic disorder, GAD, specific phobias, and alcohol use disorders. In children, high rates of oppositional defiant disorder, conduct disorder, and ADHD are both present (all of which are unique among the anxiety disorders). SP most often develops prior to other comorbid problems, but relationship with substance use disorders is more uncertain. Some studies have found substance use causing SP, while others have found the reverse. Avoidant Personality Disorder (AVPD), which involves severe restriction and avoidance of situations in which one feels that they would be judged, shows high overlap with SP, with over 40% of people with SP also meeting criteria for AVPD. It is generally more severe than SP, and some researchers claim it is just an extreme variant of SP. Other research, though, shows that there are several distinctions between the two, and that it may be more related to schizophrenia spectrum disorders.

The impact of SP is wide-ranging, both in youth and adults. It is a common reason for school refusal in youth, and the only internalizing disorder highly associated with dropping out of school early. In adults, we find reduced workplace productivity and higher unemployment rates in those with SP. Reduced health-related QoL are also found. Other problematic areas are the high rates of being single or divorced, a wide range of reported sexual dysfunctions, smaller social networks and less social support, and a lowered amount of positive psychological experiences. Persons with Sp are also at a greater risk for suicide than general population.

Child vs. Adult Presentations
SP is the anxiety disorder where the highest percentage of cases begin in childhood, with reliable and valid cases being seen as early as age six. Children are likely to show symptoms such as crying or throwing tantrums, freezing up, and staying close to a familiar person. They also can show inhibited social interactions, even up to the point of selective mutism, and may seem highly timid and uninvolved in group activities. As seen with college-aged adults, children show signs of underachievement in school settings compared to their academic and intellectual potential. Unlike adults, many children may be unable to identify the nature of their anxiety

and often do not have the option of avoiding feared situations, as they are forced into them by adults.

Gender and Cultural Differences in Presentation

Community based and epidemiological studies find that SP is slightly more represented in females (13.0% lifetime) than in males (11.1%). In most clinical and treatment-seeking samples, though, the majority of clients are males. The most commonly avoided or anxiety-provoking situations are different for males and females. For men, eating in restaurants and writing in public are seen more frequently, while in women using public restrooms and speaking in public are more represented.

In the U.S., higher rates of SP are seen among those of lower socioeconomic status, as well as persons with lower levels of education. While Native Americans are at a higher risk than Caucasians for development of SP, other minority groups show lower rates. Interestingly, people living in urban areas in both the U.S. and abroad show lower levels of SP. Cross-country comparisons show much higher rates in the U.S. (7.1% for 1-year rates) compared to non-Western nations, such as Japan (0.8%), South Korea (0.2%), urban China (0.2%), Mexico (1.7%), South Africa (1.9%). Even compared to Europe (1.1-2.3%) and Australia (1.3%), U.S. rates are much higher. When comparing Western and Asian populations, there appears to be a distinctive division between what is causing the social anxiety: fear of embarrassing self (Western) versus fear of offending others (Eastern). The culturally bound disorder of *taijin kyofusho* (TKS; translated as "fear of interpersonal relations) seen in Japan and Korea seems to exemplify this division. In TKS, people show similar avoidance patterns as SP, but do so because they fear doing something to offend another person (rather than embarrassing themselves, which is what is seen in SP). Also distinct from most cases of SP is what the individual fears they will do or present, such as having an unpleasant body odor or that they will stare at another person's crotch or chest. These features, however, have been observed in Western samples.

Epidemiology

Best evidence indicates that, in the U.S., the lifetime prevalence rate of SP for adults is 12.1%, with a 12-month prevalence rate of 7.1%. Prevalence decreases with age, from a 12-month rate of 9.1% among 18-29 year olds to 3.1% in those 60 years and above. Rates in children are relatively high due to the early onset of this disorder, with an under-18 prevalence of 6.8%. Over 50% of adults self-report retrospectively that they began having problems in childhood, and almost 80% report development of the disorder by age 20. Lower-level, non-clinical levels of SP are common, with one study showing that 20% of participants reported excessive fear of public speaking and performance, but only about 2% appeared to experience enough impairment or distress to warrant a diagnosis of SP. In the general population, most individuals with SP fear public speaking, where less than half fear speaking to strangers or meeting new people.

Etiology

As with all the other anxiety disorders, there has been significant progress in understanding the biological, psychological, and social causes of SP over the last several decades. Biologically, multiple gene variants and neurotransmitters seem to play a role in social anxiety, with no one "true" pathway to the disorder. There is only modest heritability seen in SP, less so than for OCD, but the research is still attempting to unravel if this is due to genetic linkage or shared environmental factors. What is likely is that genetics and other pre- and peri-natal biological influences are responsible for the development of a behaviorally inhibited temperament, which then places an individual at a greatly increased risk for developing SP later in life. This risk factor (behavioral inhibition) then interacts with certain types of social environments to cause someone to become social anxious. For instance, studies have found that the family environments of people diagnosed with SP tend to be more overprotective and less affectionate than is typical. Their families also tend place a very high emphasis on other people's opinions and demonstrate a distinct lack of family sociability.

Cognitive-behavioral models emphasize the psychological and learning factors that assist in developing SP. The CBT model focuses on the role of negative self and situation interpretation and avoidance. When a person with SP encounters a social situation, such as having to speak in front of an audience, this activates certain negative assumptions about themselves ("I'm no good at this, I will look foolish, no one is interested in hearing what I say"). That then causes them to perceive the situation as dangerous, not physically but socially. This activates the sympathetic nervous system, causing the outward, observable manifestations of anxiety (e.g., sweating, increased heart rate, dry mouth, feeling flushed) and at the same time making them more focused inward on themselves. In turn, this provides evidence for them that they actually *are* socially awkward, as anxiety often inhibits performance and thus causes what was feared to come true (in this case, verbal blocking, not making eye contact, looking nervous). This will feed back into negative evaluations of themselves and lead to escape and avoidance behaviors, which will cause a reduction in anxiety, negatively reinforcing those behaviors. This will also cause the person to feel that their negative cognitions concerning social situations are accurate, making them want to avoid such things in the future.

Empirically Supported Treatments
Only half of persons with SP ever seek treatment of any kind, and for those who do seek treatment, the average amount of time between onset of problems and seeking help is between 15-20 years. This is particularly sad due to the fact that both pharmacological and psychotherapeutic interventions are quite effective for this disorder. While combining the two does not appear to show benefit over either alone, the effect sizes are quite large for both medications (1.5) and cognitive-behavioral therapy (1.8). While medications tend to

decrease symptoms more quickly than CBT, the effects of CBT are slightly greater and outlast medication significantly.

The first line medical treatments for SP are the SSRIs, with the exception of fluoxetine, and the SNRIs. In particular, escitalopram and paroxetine appear to show the highest response rates (54-71% and 55-72%, respectively). Both classes are well-tolerated and have similar effect sizes compared to placebos. While the MAOIs and benzodiazepines can both be effective at lowering symptoms, they have more dangerous side effect profiles, and both carry a risk of addiction. Recently, research has also examined the use of D-cycloserine (a glutaminergic agent), but not as a standalone treatment. Instead, it appears that it may be useful as an adjunct to CBT incorporating EX/RP, increasing it's effectiveness.

Treatment for SP is longer and involves more components than for specific phobias, as the feared situations tend to be more diffuse and more anxiety-based. Gains or even improvements are seen from 6-12 months post treatment, and there are low drop-out rates (10-20%) during treatment. Both group and individual formats both show large improvement rates, but individual is higher. Given the problems with access to trained therapists, though, researchers have also examined the use of minimal contact therapies that rely heavily on self-guided exposures. One study found that bibliotherapy plus only three hours of non-therapy contact with a therapist clinically improved 40% of clients with SP. Those with severe symptoms, however, did not improve much, so this may be good option for persons with mild to moderate SP.

Six components are used in CBT addressing social anxiety: psychoeducation, applied relaxation, social skills training, imaginal and in-vivo exposure, video feedback, and cognitive restructuring. The education component helps the client to better understand the nature of social anxiety and orient them to treatment. In applied relaxation, the therapist trains clients in the use of relaxation methods such diaphragmatic breathing and progressive muscle relaxation and then has the person use them while in social situations. Social skills training focuses on improving use of verbal and non-verbal behaviors in conversations and other social situations. Video feedback involves taping the person doing a task (often public speaking) and then playing it back to them to help show them they are not acting as awkward as they believed during the task. The use of exposures appears to be the most important aspect of the treatment, as studies comparing the full CBT package to EX/RP alone have shown similar effect sizes. Likewise, applied relaxation techniques are not effective by themselves, and the same seems to be true of social skills training. Video feedback can be seen as a kind of exposure, which leaves only one other component that may play an active role in change. Cognitive restructuring is often used to help prepare for engaging in the exposures. Exposures can thus be seen as the "test" of if automatic negative thoughts are correct or incorrect. So, as the key component, exposures must be done in a very controlled manner, taking care to catch and not allow subtle avoidance or distractor behaviors and instead and focus on the situation at hand. Dichotomizing the components of EX/RP and cognitive restructuring, though, may be misleading. Observation of expert therapists treating people with SP often mix the two, rather than strictly using one or the other. As such, SP treatment is a prime example of the CBT model of behavior causing changes in thoughts, but thoughts also causing changes in behavior.

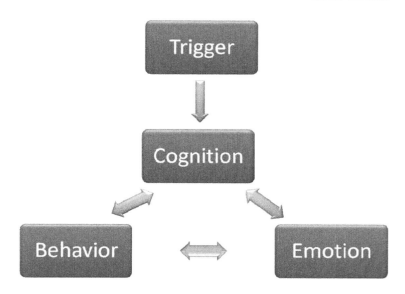

Proposed DSM-5 Revisions

The first change is the name of the disorder. In the DSM-IV, it is referred to as "Social Phobia (Social Anxiety Disorder)" while in the DSM-5 it is proposed to be renamed "Social Anxiety Disorder (Social Phobia)." This is due to the fact that the disorder appears to be one not of fear, but of anxiety. Persons with SP do not overtly and actively avoid all social interaction (which is pervasive in society) as someone with a phobia would, but instead endure such situations with marked distress and discomfort. Another significant change is the addition of two more specifiers to the current Generalized one: Performance Only and Selective Mutism. This is less supported by the research data, though, particularly the "Performance Only" subtype.

Key References

Abramowtiz, J.S., Moore, E.L., Braddock, A.E., & Harrington, D.L. (2009). Self-help cognitive–behavioral therapy with minimal therapist contact for social phobia: A controlled trial. *Journal of Behavior Therapy & Experimental Psychiatry, 40,* 98-105.

Bogels, S.M., Alden, L., Beidel, D., Clark, L.A., Pine, D.S. et al. (2010). Social anxiety disorder: Questions and answers for the DSM-V. *Depression and Anxiety, 27,* 168-189.

Kashdan, T. (2007). Social anxiety spectrum and diminished positive experiences: Theoretical synthesis and meta-analysis. *Clinical Psychology Review, 27,* 348-365.

Morris, E.P., Stewart, S.H., & Ham, L.S. (2005). The relationship between social anxiety and alcohol use disorders: A critical review. *Clinical Psychology Review, 25,* 734-760.

Stein, M.B., & Stein, D.J. (2008). Social anxiety disorder. *Lancent, 371,* 1115-1125.

Zimmerman, M., Dalrymple, K., Chelminski, I., Young, D., & Galione, J. N. (2010). Recognition of irrationality of fear and the diagnosis of social anxiety disorder and specific phobia in adults: Implications for criteria revision in DSM-5. *Depression and Anxiety, 27*(11), 1044-1049.

Panic Disorder and Agoraphobia

Of all the anxiety disorders, panic disorder is set to undergo the most changes in the proposed DSM-5. In the DSM-IV, there are three separate diagnoses, Panic Disorder with Agoraphobia, Panic Disorder without Agoraphobia, and Agoraphobia without History of Panic Disorder, while the DSM-5 proposes to have only two: Panic Disorder and Agoraphobia. As such, this section will be a bit different from the other anxiety disorders, in that I will detail information about DSM-IV panic attacks, agoraphobia, panic disorder, and then discuss the etiology, treatments, and DSM-5 changes that are proposed across all three.

Panic Attack

DSM-IV-TR Criteria

NOTE: A panic attack is not a codeable disorder. Code the specific diagnosis in which the panic attack occurs (e.g., 300.21 Panic Disorder with Agoraphobia)

A discrete period of intense fear or discomfort, in which four (or more) of the following symptoms developed abruptly and reached a peak within 10 minutes:

1. Palpitations, pounding heart, or accelerated heart rate
2. Sweating
3. Trembling or shaking
4. Sensations of shortness of breath or smothering
5. Feeling of choking
6. Chest pain or discomfort
7. Nausea or abdominal distress
8. Feeling dizzy, unsteady, lightheaded, or faint
9. De-realization (feelings of unreality) or depersonalization (being detached from oneself)
10. Fear of losing control or going crazy

67

11. Fear of dying
12. Paresthesias (numbness or tingling sensation)
13. Chills or hot flashes

Associated Features

Panic attacks (PA) are actually fairly common across all the anxiety disorders, but are especially prevalent in the phobias and post-traumatic stress disorder. They usually last several minutes and can mimic signs of a heart-attack to those not familiar with them. The most commonly reported PA symptoms are heart-pounding and dizziness, although there is great variability among PA, even in the same person (as indicated by the large number of possible symptoms). The least common symptoms (paresthesias, choking, and fear of dying) are indicative of more severe PA problems and likelihood of reoccurrence. Also, the higher number of symptoms, the more severe the PA will be. In fact, one's risk for suicide attempts and emergency room use was elevated by 20% for each additional PA symptom above the four. If a person has less than four of the PA symptoms listed above, it is referred to as a "limited panic attack."

Recent research has shown that, contrary to previous beliefs, there are not significant differences in people who are "early peakers" (symptom severity reaches highest level prior to 10 minutes) and "late peakers" (those who have highest severity after 10 minutes). This is reflected in the proposed changes for DSM-5, as discussed below. Having a PA actually puts one at an increased risk for developing other anxiety disorders, even though they are relatively common (see "Epidemiology" below).

There are three types of PA: a) unexpected or uncued panic attacks, b) situational or cued panic attacks, and c) situationally predisposed panic attacks. Unexpected or uncued are PA where the individual cannot link the onset to specific situational trigger. In contrast, a situational or cued PA occurs either in anticipation of or exposure to a specific trigger (internal or external). Finally, situationally predisposed PA are similar to a cued PA, but a person may be exposed to the triggering stimuli and *not* have a PA.

Child vs. Adult Presentations

While children can experience panic attacks, it is fairly rare. Instead, rates of reported PA begin to increase sharply during the middle teenage years and then decline rapidly starting again at age 50. Presentation does not appear to differ among age groups, although adolescents have been found to be more reluctant to discuss PA symptoms, worrying that they may represent some sort of severe medical problem.

Gender and Cultural Differences in Presentation

Studies show that more women than men that experience panic attacks, at a ratio of 2:1. Culturally, panic attacks can be seen in every ethnicity and social class. However, some studies reveal that there are differences in how the symptoms are expressed compared to Caucasians and Europeans. For example, paresthesias and fear of dying is more common among African Americans, while trembling occurs to a higher degree in Caribbean Latinos. Dizziness is a predominant symptom among several East Asian groups, with fear of dying seen more in Arabs. Finally, depersonalization, derealization, and loss of control are more often reported by Puerto Ricans than Caucasians.

Epidemiology

Almost a third of the U.S. population, 28.3%, will have at least a single panic attack at some point in their life. The overall population 12-month rate is much lower, at 11.2%, but much higher in the college population, where over 22% of students report having a PA in the past year. About 3 to 4% of adults suffer from chronic, repeated panic attacks but do not meet the DSM-IV criteria for panic disorder.

Agoraphobia

DSM-IV-TR Criteria

Agoraphobia is not a codable disorder. Code the specific disorder in which the Agoraphobia occurs (e.g., Panic Disorder With Agoraphobia or Agoraphobia Without History of Panic Disorder)

A. Anxiety about being in different places or situations from which escape might be difficult (or embarrassing), or in which help may not be available in the event of having an unexpected or situationally predisposed panic attack or panic-like symptoms. Agoraphobia fears typically involve characteristic clusters of situations that include being outside the home alone; being in a crowd or standing in a line; being on a bridge; and traveling in a bus, train, or automobile. NOTE: Consider the diagnosis of a specific phobia if the avoidance limited to one or only a few specific situations, or a social phobia if the avoidance is limited to social situations.

B. The situations are avoided (e.g. travel is restricted) or else are endured with marked distress or with anxiety about having a Panic Attack or panic like symptoms, or require the presence of a companion.

C. The anxiety or phobic avoidance is not better accounted for by another mental disorder, such as social phobia (e.g. avoidance limited to social situations because of fear of embarrassment), specific phobia (e.g. avoidance limited to a single situation like elevators), obsessive-compulsive disorder (e.g. avoidance of dirt in someone with an obsession about contamination), post-traumatic stress disorder (e.g. avoidance of stimuli associated with a severe stressor), or separated anxiety disorder (e.g. avoidance of leaving home or relatives).

D. At least four of the following symptoms developed during at least one of the attacks:

   a. Shortness of breath or a smothering sensation

b. Dizziness, unsteady feelings, faintness
c. Palpitations or accelerated heart rate
d. Trembling or shaking
e. Sweating
f. Choking
g. Nausea or abdominal distress
h. Depersonalization or derealizational
i. Flushes, hot flashes, or chills
j. Chest pain or discomfort

Associated Features

As noted above, the DSM-IV does not classify Agoraphobia (AG) as its own, distinct disorder, instead seeing it in the context of Panic Disorder. This is in sharp contrast to the ICD-10, which classifies AG as a distinct disorder. Regardless of the nosology, many agoraphobic people have fears of leaving their homes, resulting in their ability to perform normal everyday activities being severely limited. The principal symptom of AG is a fear that a panic attack will occur when the individual is in some sort of inescapable situation (e.g., crowds, tunnels, open spaces) and leave them helpless or embarrassed, even if they have never had a PA. As a result, the individual will try to avoid these situations unless there are security measures, such as a spouse or friend with them.

While most people who have PA do not develop AG, the chance to do so tends to increase with the history and frequency of them. Intriguingly, population based studies show that between 46-85% of people with AG have not actually had a full-blown PA, although this number is much lower in clinical samples (0-31%). In addition, AG is not only seen with Panic Disorder, but can be comorbid with a number of Axis I conditions. Almost 78% of people with AG qualify for at least one other anxiety disorder (phobias and GAD being the most common), while 64% are diagnosed with comorbid mood disorders and over 31% have substance abuse or dependence problems. It is also not uncommon for people diagnosed with Axis

71

II disorders, particularly avoidant and dependent personality disorders.

Child vs. Adult Presentation

Although AG usually has a first onset between 23 to 29 years, younger children and older adults can also develop it. When children develop AG, there tend to be more physical symptoms reported, so a diagnosis of an anxiety disorder may not be considered at first. Adults who are diagnosed with this disorder are commonly afraid of a *future* PA in public, and are therefore afraid of the attack itself occurring. Children, though, do not necessarily have the cognitive ability to project that far in the future, and instead may show avoidance of certain activities without a clear reason for doing so.

Gender and Cultural Differences in Presentation

There are approximately 50% more females than males that experience AG during their lifetime (1.6% vs. 1.1%), although 12-month rates are very similar (0.9% vs. 0.8%). There is some data to suggest that cultural perceptions of females is highly influential on AG, as cultures where females are viewed as more submissive and dependent on males show higher rates of AG.

Epidemiological study rates vary greatly across national studies, from a low of 0% in urban Chinese to a high of 4.8% in South Africans. In the U.S., Caucasians tend to show lower rates than minority groups, with Puerto Ricans displaying very high rates (6.0%). This is not consistent across all studies, though as some find similar rates for all groups. Minority groups do appear to have an earlier age of onset than Caucasians, as well as showing decreases in prevalence with age.

Epidemiology

Despite not being an official diagnosis in DSM-IV, best estimates are that AG has a lifetime prevalence of 1.3% in the general population. Rates of 12 month prevalence were only slightly lower at 0.9%. Other studies have found a point prevalence rate of 0.8% for panic attacks occurring with AG. Rates do not tend to decrease steadily

72

with age, but instead show a pattern of decreasing slightly from 18-29 year olds (1.0%) to 30-44 year olds (0.8%), the increasing until age 59 (1.2%), and finally greatly decreasing afterward (0.4%).

Panic Disorder (PD) with Agoraphobia (w/ AG) OR without Agoraphobia (w/o AG)

DSM-IV-TR Criteria

A. Both 1 and 2:

1. Recurrent, unexpected panic attacks
2. At least one of the following:
    i. Persistent concern about having additional attacks
    ii. Worry about the implications of the attack or its consequences (e.g. losing control, having a heart attack, "going crazy")
    iii. A significant change in behavior related to attacks.

B. Absence of agoraphobia (PD w/o AG) **OR** presence of agoraphobia (PD w/ AG)

C. The panic attacks are not due to the direct physiological effects of a substance (e.g. hyperthyroidism).

D. The panic attacks are not better accounted for by another mental disorder such as social phobia (e.g. occurring on exposure to a feared social situation), obsessive-compulsive disorder (e.g. on exposure to dirt in someone with an obsession about contamination), post-traumatic stress disorder (e.g. in response to stimuli associated with a severe stressor), or separation anxiety disorder (e.g. in response to being away from home or close relatives).

Associated Features

Many individuals with PD report having occasional or constant feelings of anxiety that are not focused on any specific event or situation, while others become apprehensive about what might happen during routine activities. The negative impacts of PD are myriad. First, demoralization is common as the person becomes discouraged, ashamed and unhappy about the difficulties of living everyday life. They blame themselves, thinking that they are lacking in "character" or "strength". Missing school or work because of medical visits is common, and can lead to dropping out of school or job loss. People with PD have very high rates of medical visits, procedures, and laboratory tests, both compared to the general public and persons with other anxiety disorders. They consistently report dissatisfaction with their medical treatment, and physicians rate people with PD as more difficult to care for. Medical visits over a 12-month period are especially common to the ER (43.9%), urgent care (48.8%), cardiologist (46.3%), and family practitioners (46.3%).

Comorbidity is higher for people who have combined PD and AG, compared to those with PD alone. In PD w/ AG, over 93% meet criteria for another anxiety disorder, while the overlap is only 66% in PD w/o AG. Similar differences are seen in comorbid mood disorder (73% vs. 50%) and substance abuse problem (37% vs. 27%) rates. Depression is a very comorbid, but can either precede (a third of cases) or occur after PD (two thirds of cases).

Child vs. Adult Presentation

While both children and adults can have PD, it tends to be very rare before puberty, gradually increases until middle age, and then decreases again. Youth and adults experience similar symptoms (trembling, breaking out in a sweat, heart, palpitations, nausea, and so on), although adolescents report worrying about subsequent PA less than young adults. It is crucial to note that some researchers have found that children who are later highly prone to developing

PD display much higher rates of separation anxiety than same-age peers. Such children also tend to show other anxious behaviors, such as behavioral inhibition and anxiety-sensitivity.

Gender and Cultural Differences in Presentation

PD w/o AG is two times more common in women than in men, while PD w/ AG is three times more common in women. This gender gap begins to be observable by early adolescence, and just continues to widen with age. It is important to note that some cultural or ethnic groups restrict women from being in the public life, and that this should be distinguished from agoraphobia. PD appears to be more debilitating to women than it is for men, as females tend to become more depressed, rate higher on fear tests, and spend more time avoiding social situations. Men are also more likely to hold down a steady job.

In the U.S., minorities tend to have lower rates of PD than Caucasians, although Native American groups have been found to have higher rates. Cross-culturally, lower rates of PD are seen outside the U.S., even in European samples. For instance, studies in the Ukraine have found rates of 1.27% and 1.94% for 12-month and lifetime, respectively. Germany had slightly higher 12-month rates (1.8%), but still lower than the U.S, while Australia was even lower (1.1%). In Japan (0.5% for 12-month), South Korea (0.2%), China (0.2%), PD is extremely rare, with similarly low rates in other non-Western countries (0.6% in Mexico, 0.8% in South Africa).

As noted earlier, certain symptoms of PA are more or less frequently seen in certain cultural groups. Directly related to PD are several culturally-bound disorders. For example, *khyâl* attacks in Cambodia are characterized by a mix of PA and culture-specific symptoms including tinnitus and neck soreness w/ dizziness. *Ataque de nervios* ("attack of nerves") among Latin Americans and *trunggio* ("wind")-related attacks in Vietnam also appear to be culturally-relevant variations on PD.

Epidemiology

Panic disorder (with or without agoraphobia) has a lifetime prevalence rate of 4.7% in the U.S., with a 12-month rate of 2.7%. Both lifetime and one year rates show an upside down U curve of distribution, with lower rates for 18-29 year olds (4.2% and 2.8%) and those over 60 years old (2.1% and 0.8%) compared to age groups of 30-44 (5.9% and 3.7%) and 45-59 (5.9% and 3.1%). Rates for children and adolescents are very low, likely due to the lack of development of cognitive abilities such as self-monitoring and metacognition.

In treatment-seeking clinical settings, the prevalence rates for panic disorder are noticeably higher, with some studies finding as high as 30%. In general medical settings, almost 10% of people referred for a mental health consultation were diagnosed with panic disorder. In specialty medical settings such as vestibular, respiratory, and neurology clinics the prevalence rates vary from 10% and 30%, while in cardiology clinics rates as high as 60% have been found. In community samples, a third to a half of individuals diagnosed with PD have AG as well. There is a much higher rate of PD w/ AG encountered in clinical samples than without AG.

Etiology

Genetic and family studies have found that both biology and environment are strong contributors to the development of both PD and AG. Twin studies have revealed that there is a genetic link to the development of PD. Individuals with a first degree relative suffering from panic disorder are eight times more likely to develop panic disorder than people without. If onset is before age 20, though, the individual's risk increases to 20 times as likely to develop PD. Heritability for PD seems to be around 45%, with shared (10%) and unshared (45%) environments contributing significantly. For AG, heritability estimates are slightly higher, at around 60%. The temperament trait of behavioral inhibition (BI) is highly implicated in the development of both, and parents with PD or AG are more likely to have children who are behavioral inhibited. This, however, holds true across all anxiety disorders. For PD and AG specifically, anxiety sensitivity (believing anxiety is harmful and bad) is the key trait. Furthermore, we know that early trauma and maltreatment are risk factors for developing both later, and that development may be meditated by the presence of BI.

Neurologically, panic attacks are closely linked to amygdala function. The amygdala is the anxiety "way-station" that mediates incoming stimuli from the environment (thalamus and sensory cortex) and stored experience (frontal cortex and hippocampus). As such, it impacts the anxiety and panic response by stimulating various brain areas responsible for key panic symptoms based on both internal and external stimuli and past events. In particular, the periaqeductal gray in the midbrain could be especially important for mediating panic symptoms. Pharmacology and CBT can effectively treat PA, but they act on different systems. While pharmacology can target all areas of the above described system, effecting amygdala and frontal-lobe interpretation of stimuli or output effects, CBT impacts the frontal-lobe areas, especially in the medial prefrontal cortex, which is known to inhibit input to the amygdala.

Psychologically, the major factor in the development of PD and AG seems to be anxiety sensitivity. This is the belief, which could be acquired in any number of ways, that anxiety could cause severe physical, social, and psychological consequences that extend beyond any discomfort during a PA. Examples of means of acquisition are direct experience, vicarious observations, information transmission, and parental reinforcement. Essentially, a person develops a "fear of fear." This model posits that an individual who has a PA or PA symptoms may, through the process of interoceptive conditioning, learn to fear any change in physiological state that could signal the onset of panic. As such, they pay more attention to physical and bodily changes than most individuals, which ironically puts them at a higher risk of having panic attacks. For example, if you take the stairs to the third floor of a building, you may notice that you are flushed, breathing more heavily than usual, and sweating. For a person prone to PA, these signs would be seen as indicative of an oncoming PA rather than just being a sign of tiredness or being out of shape. This would make them nervous about the chance of having a PA, which activates the sympathetic nervous system and in turn makes it *more* likely they will actually have a PA. This can lead both to the avoidance of situations likely to trigger such sensations (AG) as well as a high likelihood of having repeated PA (PD).

Empirically Supported Treatments

Pharmacology meta-analyses for PD and AG show similar medium to large effect sizes (0.48-0.55) for both the tricyclic antidepressants (TCA) and SSRI classes of drugs. Benzodiazipines (BZD) are also effective at reducing incidence of PA, but they and the TCA are prescribed less than SSRI due to side-effect reasons. In treatment-refractory patients, SSRIs can be supplemented with BZD, or MAOIs can be used. Again, these are not front-line treatments due to their larger side effect profile. Clients should be made aware that there is a substantial (25-50%) relapse rate within 6 months when medications are discontinued, though. This may be partially due to the high potential for withdraw symptoms (from any medication) to become interoceptive cues for a PA, thus reversing the progress made while on the medication.

Cognitive-behavioral therapy is the most well studied and validated treatment for PD, with effect sizes of 0.9-1.55. It has been found to be equally effective in individual or group format, as well as in standard (14-18 meetings) or brief (6-8) sessions. As with all CBT treatments for anxiety, though, there is a massive underutilization due to lack of properly trained mental health professionals. CBT for PD emphasizes psychoeducation about panic symptoms, cognitive restructuring focusing on reducing anxiety sensivity, interoceptive exposure to feared bodily sensations, and in vivo exposure to the previously avoided and feared situations. Similar to other treatments discussed above, retraining of breathing to help patients cope with their panic and anxiety has been found to be unnecessary. CBT for

AG is very similar, but with a smaller focus on interoceptive exposures and greater emphasis on in vivo exposure to feared situations.

Although both medical and psychotherapeutic treatments are effective alone, CBT has a stronger initial effect size and yields larger long-term effect sizes (0.88-0.99 vs. 0.40-0.55). Research has found no benefit for combining the two, as controlled trials show that CBT alone is as effective as the combination. As with several other disorders, researchers have also examined self-guided therapies based on CBT, using both bibliotherapy and computer-mediated models. Results are generally supportive, with one study finding similar one-year effect sizes for 10 session live CBT (0.93) and 10 module internet self-help treatment (0.80).

Proposed DSM-5 Revisions

As mentioned earlier, there are major changes proposed for these disorders in DSM-5. First, Agoraphobia is recommended to be classified as a distinct disorder. There are three primary lines of evidence that have supported this change: psychometric evaluations supporting the construct of agoraphobia alone, epidemiological investigations of prevalence, and the impact AG has on clinical course and outcome. This change would also bring the DSM-5 and the ICD (International Classifications of Disease) more into alignment, as Agoraphobia is already a separate disorder in that system. As such, Panic Disorder would no longer have the "with or without Agoraphobia" included in the diagnosis. It is also proposed that a specifier be added to all the anxiety disorders that would allow "with panic attacks" to be noted in the diagnosis, given the high rate of PA across the class.

Key References

Bakker, A., van Balkom, A.J., Spinhoven, P. (2002). SSRIs vs. TCAs in the treatment of panic disorder: a meta-analysis. *Acta Psychiatric Scandinavia, 106*(3), 163-167.

Craske, M.G., Kircanski, K., Epstein, A., Wittchen, H-U., Pine, D.S. et al. (2010). Panic Disorder: A review of DSM-IV Panic Disorder and proposals for DSM-V. *Depression and Anxiety, 27,* 93-112.

Deacon, B., Lickel, J., & Abramowitz, J. S. (2008). Medical utilization across the anxiety disorders. *Journal of Anxiety Disorders, 22*(2), 344-350.

Kiropoulos, L.A., Kleina, B., Austina, D.W., Gilsona, K., Piera, C., et al. (2008). Is internet-based CBT for panic disorder and agoraphobia as effective as face-to-face CBT? *Journal of Anxiety Disorder, 22,* 1273-1284.

Schmidt, N.B., Keough, M.E. (2010). Treatment of panic. Annual Review of Clinical Psychology, 27(6), 241-256.

Roy-Byrne, P.P., Craske, M.G., & Stein, M.B. (2006). Panic disorder. *Lancet, 368,* 1023-1032.
Wittchen, H-U., Gloster, A.T., Beesdo-Baum, K., Fava, G.A., & Craske, M.G. (2010). Agoraphobia: A review of the diagnostic classificatory position and criteria. *Depression and Anxiety, 27,* 113-133.

Other Anxiety Disorders

In addition the disorders reviewed above, there are three others included in the DSM-IV anxiety disorder section. The first is *Anxiety Disorder Due to a General Medical Condition*. As expected from the name, this is where a person experience anxiety problems as a direct result of a medical problem, such as as hyperthyroidism, hypothyroidism, vitamin deficiencies, or brain lesions. People with cardiovascular problems, endocrine disorders, neurologic conditions, peptic ulcers, diabetes, and respiratory conditions are also at risk of developing anxiety as a result of their condition.

The second is *Substance-Induced Anxiety Disorder*, which is the direct result of either intoxication or withdrawal from a psychoactive substance. Common substances causing such problems include alcohol, cocaine, sedatives, hypnotics, and anxiolytics.

The final is *Anxiety Disorder Not Otherwise Specified*. This is a "catch-all" category, where a person displays prominent anxiety symptoms or avoidance, but does not meet full criteria for any of the other, specific disorders.

Lightning Source UK Ltd.
Milton Keynes UK
UKOW06f1852081015

260136UK00017B/603/P